$17.95

PRAISE FOR

*Lines of*
# Convergence
*Prose & Poetry*

Mr. Bigelow has done it again! This collection is so real and covers everything from romance and good friends to depression and personal struggles–this book takes you on a journey! The short stories and captivating and the poetry is delightful. *Lines of Convergence* has something for everyone.

Nika Ackenbom

In *Lines of Convergence*, Bigelow's mastery of storytelling is on display. He carries the reader from lively, entertaining banter to gripping inspirational stories to the dark recesses of depression. Whether the subject is dark or light, the characters compel us to read on into the night. Many of his poems drive home the themes of the stories. Another convergence.

Gerry Kruger. author of *On Kruger Pond: Charlie's Legacy*, *TWO OF US: A Father-Daughter Memoir* and others

*Lines of Convergence* by Alden Bigelow is a wonderful book to discover the breadth of this talented author's work. In this compendium, he has included some of his best formerly published work–chapters, scenes, short stories, and poems. He writes about believable characters who have dreams, disappointments and despair. They confront sad times, challenging circumstances and even bad luck, but they do it with charm, hope, and kindness. Read this book and meet them.

Elaine Ruggieri, author of *Retreat at St. Jerome's*

The more I read, the more I realize how well Alden Bigelow writes. Read this book and enjoy the writing.

Marjorie Adams Bigelow

In *Lines of Convergence*, Alden Bigelow presents a series of short stories and poems that are highly entertaining and thought-provoking. His engaging writing style and cast of colorful characters draw the reader in from the first page and hold one's attention throughout this series of vignettes and moving poetry. Descriptive scenes evoke images of places and adventures from days gone by, including a fascinating fictional conversation among Thomas Jefferson and his contemporaries. Alden's previous works set a high bar of quality, and *Lines of Convergence* continues his standard of literary excellence.

Fred Shackleford, author of *The Ticket*

Alden Bigelow's *Lines of Convergence* brings together warm stories of dear friends and favorite pets. It also brings life's difficulties. Dreamy days in Nantucket are brought to life with well written characters. All is blended into a wonderful experience for any reader.

Cheryl Schwandt

## ALSO BY ALDEN E. C. BIGELOW

### Waiting on Nantucket

*Waiting on Nantucket* is a poignant memoir of a struggling writer who drifts among a cast of fascinating characters on a magical island. Alden Bigelow's characters come alive in this masterful, eloquent, and engaging tale. He hit it out of the park!

Fred Shackleford, author of *The Ticket*

### The Great American Mammal Jamboree

*The Great American Mammal Jamboree* tells the mythical story of how the animal mammals mysteriously acquire the cloak of invisibility (to Man) and gather at a mystical sanctuary, also invisible to Man. Here they establish a new code of ethics for living. They strengthen their camaraderie by participating in Mammal Olympics. Over time they learn the true meaning of trust and faith, of sacrifice, and love and understanding.

### Killing Time in a Small Southern Town

*Killing Time* is the fictional re-telling of a White on Black kidnapping which took place in Charlottesville, Virginia in the segregationist charged days of 1962. It deals with the violence and turmoil associated with the integration of a self-styled sophisticated University town. It is the story of a society struggling to come to grips with the nature of the Jeffersonian concept of freedom and the inherent equality of all men before the law.

### Growing Up with Jemima

From the innocence of the early days as the Lone Ranger, Tonto, and his trusty cocker spaniel sidekick making Charlottesville safe and happy, to the coming of age in Richmond with the hard truth, these are the early adventures of a boy who learns early on that life may be overrated, but a good dog will never let you down.

### Norton's Lament

*Norton's Lament* is the sometimes fictional autobiographical life struggle between faith and reality, love and hate … you know, life. It may be your struggle, too.

### I Have My Reasons
#### Audio CD

A musical celebration of some of Bigelow's favorite people and in honor of some of his favorite dogs.

www.AldenBigelow.com

## IN MEMORY OF
## JOHN COATES (1946-2022)

He was a good friend who brought joy and enthusiasm to all of us who knew him. Despite many physical challenges, he remained undefeated and untied, whether through inspirational teaching or triumph at a life well-lived.

## DEDICATION

To Marjorie, still my best friend and confidant. There's only one Marjorie.

## ACKNOWLEDGEMENT & THANKS

- to Kandy Harvey, once again, for her excellent layout, design, planning partnership and her friendship.

- to Nika Ackenbom, for all the productive facets and great attitude. She's my favorite associate.

- to my wonderful readers, Nika Ackenbom, Wat Ellerson, Hugh Gildea, Gerry Kruger, Elaine Ruggieri, Cheryl Schwandt, Fred Shackelford, and M.E.A Bigelow.

- to my best friends and dogs of distinction, Jemima, Hakim, Verushka, Snookums, Jemima 2, Benjamin, Justin, Gus, Mystery, Spanky, you betcha, Jack, Quincy, Daisy, Elvis, Buddy Holly, Chowder, Homer, Goose, and Tyler who loves Mary, 2020.

BE Unlimited Publishing • Palmyra, VA

*Lines of*
# Convergence
*Prose & Poetry*

ALDEN E. C. BIGELOW

*A definition of*
## PROSE

A short work of fiction dealing with a few characters and a single event.

*As for my prose…*When I write a short story, my mind-set is as follows: I cannot paint, but with words I can paint the pictures. It is always my goal to create a visual in the minds of my audience, perhaps persuade them to an idea, but to always entertain. Since a short story does not allow the luxury of developing a character or plot beyond a few pages, the goal is to always plant the idea for a single event upon which everything turns. In writing short stories there are challenges of brevity, unlike in writing the novel. For a writer who is considering the art of the short story, I would simply tell them to go read O.Henry, Edgar Allen Poe, Mark Twain—so many more—like mine.

All you need to get started is a pen, some paper and your imagination. Then start writing. Poof! Now you're a writer. Advance your story from there.

*A definition of*
## POETRY

An official definition of poetry is an arrangement of words of rhythmical composition, sometimes rhymed, more imaginative than speech or prose.

*In my poetry…*I try to share some truth, give it rhythm, and hope the odd rhyme doesn't get in the way.

# PROSE

## Other Stories

# POETRY

**Adapted from**

*Growing Up with Jemima*

## SOOKEY'S GIFT

I remember that day in 1952 when Johnny B. Goode drove out to meet with my Dad. At six years old, I was excited to be sitting in the open rumble seat of Dad's red Ford Model A roadster, so I could hear everything when Mr. Goode drove up to the entrance of the farm where we were parked.

"Yes, sir. Here it is," said Johnny brightly. "A 1942 Lincoln Continental. Drives real good and clean as a whistle. And I just lowered the price of the car to 300 dollars 'cause… well, I need the money. Whaddaya say?"

Dad smiled and walked around the black Lincoln with the red leather seats. At the same time, he sized up Mr. Goode who was a red faced, wiry little fellow with blonde hair and hard blue eyes. He was dressed in khaki pants and shoes, both probably Army issued. Dad turned from the car to face Mr. Goode. "You were in the Army?"

"Yes, sir. Three years… just got out last year. Corporal first class. Army was good to me."

"Well, that's fine," said Dad. "I was in the Army too. Where are you from?"

"Way up in those hills," said Johnny, pointing up to the Blue Ridge Mountains spreading out above us. "Grew up on a little farm, a lot like this one. It wasn't much, but we got by."

"Oh," Dad smiled. "So you know something about farming?"

"Heck yes. When I was a boy, we had a milking cow. We had a garden that provided us just about everything we could eat, except for meat we got from hunting."

Johnny stared at my Dad. He then scuffed the ground with the heel of his boot.

"Why do you ask? I thought you was wantin' to buy my Lincoln Continental."

Dad moved up close to Mr. Goode and put a hand on his shoulder. "Well, Johnny, This is a fine car you have here. It is definitely a Lincoln. But it is not a Lincoln Continental, and that's the model I was interested in."

Johnny's shoulders slumped as he pulled back. "The man who sold it to me said it was a Continental — I guess I didn't know the difference — now I guess you don't want the car. Oh, Lord. What am I gonna tell Dorothy?"

He reached to open the door of his car as if to drive away.

"Hold on there," said Dad. "I might have something you would be interested in — even better than selling your car to me."

Johnny B. Goode looked down at the ground and started once again to kick at the hard scrabble clay beneath his feet. He looked weary. "Look, mister, all I got is this car and the rent's coming due and I just lost my job. My wife Dorothy's eight months pregnant and we're gonna get kicked out. If you ain't gonna buy this car from me, what the heck else can you do for me?"

He dropped his head and looked down at the ground.

"Well, Johnny, you said you grew up farming, is that right?"

"Yes, sir," said Johnny slowly.

"Well, see that little, white clapboard cottage up on the hill there?" said Dad, pointing in that direction. "What you see is a two-bedroom cottage with a fenced-in yard."

"Yeah, I see it," Johnny said evenly.

"Well," Dad said. "It needs a little fixing up, but it's got a working wood stove and you can pump water from a well just outside… and you can move in today if you want to."

"I told you I ain't got no money," Johnny said slowly.

"I'm not looking for money, Johnny. I am looking for a tenant farmer. I'm planning on bringing in some laying chickens and a milk cow and we're gonna start a garden in this plot of ground right here. Are you interested? If you are willing to milk that cow, take care of general upkeep, and bring in the eggs from those chickens, if your wife would be willing to work the garden with my wife, here's what I'll do. I'll split everything with you right down the middle – no cost to you – you can have the cottage rent free and I will pay for any materials you need to fix it up. "Now, how does that sound?"

"Why me?" Johnny was still a little suspicious.

"Because I know you're a good man and I can see you learned a lot in the Army too  –  I can size up a man pretty well and I'm wagering you're hardworking and just want a chance.

"So, I want to take that chance on you. You won't let me down, will you?"

Johnny B. Goode straightened up as a smile lit up his face. "No, sir. I won't let you down."

They shook hands on it.

"All right then. So… when would you like to move in?"

"Would this afternoon be too soon?"

"No, Johnny. That would be just fine."

### Our New Friend

Sookey came to us as a calf, a color of orange and red, the same as the hard clay beneath us. She had a little triangular patch of white, as if it were painted on her breastbone. My brother and I laughed as she literally stumbled down the ramp from the pickup truck and began looking around as if to inspect everything around her… no fear, just curiosity. She pulled up some yellowish grass and began chewing it thoughtfully.

Looking around, she saw us for the first time, trickled on over and dropped her head to sniff our sneakers and then our jeans. She raised her head and looked at me straight in the eyes  –  me!  –  I was a little scared but, "she was only the size of a large dog" I thought, so I tiptoed over to her. I was still nervous, but I sensed she would not hurt me. I began to rub my hand up and down her furry head. She moved in closer and gently pushed against my chest. Then she turned her side to me, it seemed, so that I could give her a full rub down. I reached over the top of her back and then down her side to her tummy below, back and forth. It was kind of a belly rub.

After a few moments, Sookey, as she came to be called serendipitously, suddenly pulled back, looked me in the eye again and began to turn round and round. Then she came back and pressed her head up against me again.

It was right about this time, she spotted my mother walking up from the garden below. Mom had something in her hand, a stunted and stringy carrot which she had brought up from the first year's crop of her vegetable garden. Mom flattened her hand and offered it to Sookey, who I was afraid would reject this pitiful offering out of hand. In fact, she vacuumed it down immediately, looking at my mother for more of the same.

Mom laughed and started walking down the path to her garden again, only to see that Sookey was trotting along right behind her. Believing, I guess, that wherever my mother went there would be more of these delectable mangy carrots. About this time Mom opened up the gate to one of our fenced in fields. With little encouragement, Sookey raced off into it, having spotted tall grass, honeysuckle and a veritable smorgasbord of other tasty delights that awaited her.

Well, that's how we met Sookey, and how she became an instant part of our family. As the years went by she gave us her heart and her humor. All too soon she also brought us the gift of a new life, even as she lost her own.

### The Bloat

As time went by, Sookey, who was allowed the freedom to roam around the farm, would often appear when Mom and Mrs. Goode were tending the garden – possibly in hopes of receiving one of those special carrots – but just as likely because she wanted to be around us.

Even as she grew bigger – much bigger – and was mated to a young bull, she did not alter her routine except for the daily milking. She would wander on up to the barnyard just behind the Goode house at about the same time every day and wait to be milked… because we needed the milk and Sookey needed to be milked.

Even as a young kid, I was fascinated to watch Mrs. Goode sitting on a three-legged stool with a large metal bucket placed under Sookey and then pulling the giant fingers she called "teats" and began the piston like action up and down, allowing the spigots of milk to splash into the pail and fill it nearly to the top. During this procedure, Sookey would sometimes turn her head to watch Mrs. Goode complete the job.

"Good girl, Sookey," Mrs. Goode would say as she stood up and pulled out her stool and pail of milk from under and gave her a pat on the rump. Then Mrs. Goode would reach into her apron and pull up one of those "special" carrots and offer it to Sookey, who gently nibbled it out of her hand. With her tail swishing behind her, Sookey would wander off into the fields to resume grazing, but sometimes she would lie down, right there on her side in the barnyard so that we kids could just climb all over her. She was a regular jungle gym. She loved it and so did we.

As a young kid, I found the farm so interesting as there were always exciting things going on that I had not been exposed to in the city.

In the second year we were on the farm, Mom and Dad decided to dam up a creek that ran through the property to create a small lake. This is where I learned to swim. Dad built a pier and even constructed a floating pontoon raft. He secured it about fifty yards away from the pier and dropped a large cinder block wrapped in wire nineteen feet to the bottom of the lake in order to secure it.

Before long, my friends and I would dive off that pier into the cold water and swim out to the pontoon raft to play Marco Polo and other games. Sometimes during the games, I would look over to the bank nearby and see Sookey having a drink of the muddy water. She would look up, see me, flick her tail and then proceed to get another drink. I know that flicking tail was her way of telling me hello, and I still believe that.

---

When Sookey swelled up with her first calf, Mom explained the fundamental process to my tender nine-year-old ears. Sookey had been "mated" to a bull so that "she could bring milk to us through the whole process of birthing a calf. The process would repeat every year," she said.

Though I did not know exactly what "mating" meant, I decided that I knew enough for my purposes and so I did not ask Mom for any more information. I sensed Mom understood this as well.

But what I did know was that now we were going to have our own calf that Sookey would bring to us. Now *that* was exciting.

One day, when we knew Sookey was about to give birth to this, her first calf, she disappeared and we could not find her. My parents were worried that she may have gone off to give birth on her own and had hidden herself and the calf to protect it. This was not an unusual thing, but it was important to find Sookey to make sure that she was okay, as well as her infant offspring.

She did not resurface for three days after disappearing. It is amazing even on twenty-five acres how a large animal can find a nook in the woods or in the fields, be really quiet and not move, and be very hard to find. Usually, if not found, they would reappear and lead you to the calf. In this case, it did not happen.

We were all worried, adults and children, because Sookey was family.

On the fourth day, we were about to begin an intensive search of every part of our farm, as well as the neighboring farms. All of our neighbors were also on the lookout for Sookey.

I remember her return so well. I had swum off the dock to hang out on the pontoon raft when I spotted her just behind the Japanese tea house Dad had built on the dock the previous year. She had settled down on the dam behind it and I could see she was trembling. I swam back to the dock as fast as I could and raced to her side. She had settled on the ground awkwardly. She was breathing hard and her eyes were closed.

I called out to my Mom, who was just below the dam with Mrs. Goode doing their usual gardening. Mom walked up the hill quickly and after one look at Sookey, she told me to stay there while she raced to the phone at Mrs. Goode's house and called Tim Lupton. He was a friend and farmer who lived nearby. He was there in ten minutes and examined Sookey closely.

"Bloat," he said. "She's got the bloat. Must have eaten some poison grass."

I noticed at this time how big and swollen Sookey's stomach was.

"We've got to relieve the pressure on her or she will die," said Tim. "It might kill the calf, but maybe we can save her life."

He produced a large, old pocket knife and peeled out the hole puncher designed to pierce leather so as to make a hole in it, as for a leather belt.

Tim was a big man. I watched him pull back his right arm with the hole puncher sticking out of his hand and I watched him plunge it into Sookey's stomach.

In an instant, I could hear the whooshing sound of stale, stank air rapidly escaping from the inside of Sookey's belly. She turned her head to us and tried to get up. She could not. Her front legs were churning, but she could not roll over. Her head fell back to the ground and somehow, I knew that she was gone.

"The combination of carrying that calf and the poisoned vegetation which she ate and gave her the bloat... well, I guess she couldn't recover," said Tim. "I think the calf is still in her, probably would have been stillborn anyway. If you'd like, I'll come back in my tractor and dig a hole below the dam here and we will put her in it. But we need to do it today. Otherwise, the buzzards and all manner of varmints will come to have her for their next meal."

---

Two days later, Mrs. Goode told Mom that she kept hearing strange noises coming from the back five acres of our farm that was so full of briars and weeds and poison ivy that no one ever went there.

"That's where the noise is coming from," said Mrs. Goode.

"Well," said Mom. "let's put on our boots and walk on over there to see what we can find."

What they found was Sookey's calf whom she had apparently birthed and hidden from all intruders until she could assure herself that all was safe so that she could bring us, her people, back to take care of her newborn. But she never did because she died of the bloat and we never looked for a calf because we thought the calf had died inside of her bloated stomach before she could birth it.

Still, in all, Sookey had found a way to bring us a gift, a calf we called Rosie. A calf who grew to bring us many years of milk and laughter.

We came to know that she was Sookey's parting gift to us...to love and enjoy in her thereafter.

**Ode to Sookey**

And so she left us, secretly,
an infant calf called Rosie,
who brought us creamy milk and fun,
just as Sookey had done
all those years ago.
It was just as if
she was Sookey's gift,
... as she was.

Jemima.

## ALBEMARLE BEAGLES FOR CHRISTMAS

It was Christmas in 1955, a time full of hope for Jemima and me. Of course, any day with a full food bowl and the odd squirrel to chase was always a good day for Jemima. As for me, I was tired of finishing last in various neighborhood bike races to my taller, speedier pals. And who can maintain discipline in his gang if he has to do so from ten yards behind?

I had been studying the Montgomery Ward catalogue and its advertisement for a 3-speed Schwinn Super Cobra on page 78. It could make me the fastest kid in my neighborhood, I hoped, because no one else had a three speed like this… and with the sound of those new Bicycle plastic playing cards strategically flapping in my spokes, I might have the fastest and loudest bicycle on Rugby Avenue. Man alive.

Unfortunately, my Christmas wish presentation did not go as well with my father as it had in my head. "I understand, Robin. I will buy you those special plastic playing cards so you can attach them to your spokes and liven up your bike. But I'm afraid you're going to have to settle for the loudest bike on the block, not the fastest — your one speed Huffy 102 will get you through 1956."

Just then Mr. Johnny B. Goode, the tenant farmer of our 25-acre hardscrabble farm we owned just south of town, appeared at the door. He was wearing an old fedora. The brim was sagging and the cold December rain fell around his face. He looked agitated.

"Come on in, Johnny," said Dad. "What's on your mind? How's Sookey the cow and all our free-range chickens you're raising? Is that old rooster boy doing his job? Do you have some eggs for me?"

"I can't rightly talk about that tonight, Mr. B. If you don't mind, I got more pressin' matters on my mind."

My dad and I could see that Johnny B. Goode was pretty upset about something. "Something's got you riled up," Dad said. "Here," he beckoned Mr. Goode inside. "Come on in out of the rain and tell us about it."

Mr. Goode edged into the hallway. He was soaked through but he wouldn't take off his World War II Great Coat to dry off. "Thank you, Mr. B., I'll just keep my coat on. I can't stay long. I got to get home soon before Dorothy does something terrible."

"Now what would your sweet wife do that wouldn't be good for you or those four little munchkins you've got? You haven't been getting into those quart bottles of Arrow 77 Beer again have you?" Dad said this with a knowing wink. A little overdrinking was acceptable between men in those days as long as you took care of your family and it didn't get out of hand.

"No, nothing like that," Mr. Goode began. "Dorothy's practically cured me of that. Kept me out of our bedroom for two weeks last September, if you know what I mean." (I didn't know what he meant, but there was a smile on Dad's face, so I guess he did.)

"Anyway," Johnny continued, "I've cut way down on my Arrow 77 and even the kids seem happier, so that's all good, but now Dorothy wants to drown all of Brownie's Hound Dog litter. Now I can't have that."

Both Dad and I could see that Johnny B. Goode was getting pretty worked up. He took off his soaked fedora hat and began running his hands through his thin blond hair which he had apparently slicked back with the ever popular Wildroot Cream Oil.

"Now hold on there, Johnny," said Dad. "There's got to be a reason for all this. Let's make some sense of it. I'm sure we can work something out."

I could see Mr. Goode relax a little and he stopped banging his hat against his knees. He was looking at Dad. I sure hoped Dad had a solution. But why would Mrs. Goode, of all people, want to drown Brownie's pups?

"Now look, Johnny," Dad continued. "You and I both know Mrs. Goode is a fine woman. We also know that she's great with animals from Sookey, milking her twice a day in her time, to taking care of the chickens … and she loves that "Heinz 57" mutt Brownie. Why would she do anything to her pups? Answer me that and we'll get to the heart of the problem."

"Well, that's just it Mr. B. Dorothy tells me she loves all animals, but she also says she's a practical woman. This is Brownie's seventh litter. And Dorothy just bought us a genuine two-ply carpet. She ordered it through the Montgomery Ward catalogue. It comes in on Monday. She says if I don't get rid of those pups by Monday when the rug comes in, she's gonna have to get rid of them all before Brownie sneaks 'em into the house like she always does, and they ruin the carpet. So, Dorothy says if the pups ain't gone by Monday she'll have to drown 'em in the creek. Now I can't have that. I've already tried to give 'em away. Dorothy's sister Helen says they're the ugliest pups she's ever seen and she won't take one even if we paid her."

Jemima retreated under the hallway table and began a low growl. Even in her liver and white 30-lb Cocker Spaniel cuteness, she could look pretty fierce when she bared her teeth. She did not approve of raised voices, except for mine, and she was a little alarmed.

"Easy girl," chuckled my dad. "Johnny's got a little problem here and we're going to help him solve it. Right, Robin?" I grinned in approval, with the faith of a nine-year-old that Dad could solve just about anything.

Then Dad turned back to Mr. Goode. He had a big grin on his face. "I've got it. I've got the solution, Johnny. Now you go on home to Mrs. Goode and tell her not to drown those pups because we're going to sell them."

"How are we gonna sell 'em, Mr. B.? I told you I can't even give 'em away."

"Just listen to me, Johnny. You bring those pups to me right here on Rugby Avenue on Saturday morning. I guarantee you that I will sell them all. If I don't, I will keep them myself."

I thought I heard a small growl at this coming from Jemima's direction.

"Not only that, I will split the profits with you. Your share should be about $12.50. Maybe you can buy Mrs. Goode that special dress you say she's wanted from Leggett's Bargain Center."

Johnny B. Goode grinned and gave my Dad a hearty handshake. "Oh, this is great Mr. B. You promise you'll keep the litter no matter what?"

"Yep. Just bring 'em here Saturday morning right about 6:00 AM. And don't let Mrs. Goode drown 'em in the river between now and then."

"Wow. You'll sell the pups and I'll get some money too. I really can buy Dorothy that Christmas dress. This is great. I don't know how you are gonna do it, but I believe you. Hey, I think I'll go get me some Arrow 77 to celebrate!"

"Uh, I think you better hold off on the celebration until you deliver the pups, Johnny," said Dad. "Mrs. Goode might not be as trusting or understanding while she's still taking care of all those pups."

"Yeah, you got that right Mr. B. She's a good woman, but she's been a little touchy lately with four kids under five and now those pups. I'll go real easy, and I'll deliver those pups Saturday morning. Hmm, I sure don't know how you're gonna do it, but they're your pups no matter what come Saturday morning, right?"

"Right," repeated Dad. "All right, Johnny. Don't worry about a thing. Just do your part."

"Oh, yes, sir. I sure will Mr. B. I'll see you this weekend." Johnny B. Goode, a happy man, hummed his way out the front door into the rain.

"That was great, Dad," I beamed up at my father as Jemima wiggled out from under the table. "But how are you going to sell five ugly pups that Mr. Goode couldn't give away?"

"Never mind about that, Robin," Dad said with a wink. "Now you're a little too young for this kind of salesmanship. Go get your big brother, and I'll teach him how to sell Albemarle Beagles."

"OK," I said slowly as I traipsed off to find my 11-year old brother. He was in our bedroom trying to "rock the cradle" with his six-diamond deluxe Domino yo-yo.

"What's on your mind, Chester?" he asked as he did a quick yo-yo "walk the dog" and "holstered" his yo-yo as it sprang up the string and into his pocket. My brother liked to pretend he was Marshall Matt Dillon of Gunsmoke and I sometimes played his trusty, limping and uncoordinated deputy, Chester. It was actually pretty much fun. I had the limp down pretty good and we shared many shots of Bar Room Kool-Aid as we celebrated the bad guys we had run out of town.

"No time for that, Mr. Dillon!!" I said in my best Chester Texas drawl. "Dad wants you in the living room."

"Why? Is it something bad? Does he know about the garter snake I let out under your bed? You didn't tell on me, did you?"

"No. You're on your own there. This is about some extra chore he wants you to do Saturday morning. Hey, if you don't want to, I don't mind doing it for you. Jemima and I get up early anyway."

"Hey, thanks," said my big brother. "Saturday morning, I watch my favorite western, Wild Bill Hickok, on tv. You know, the one where I play him and you get to be his slightly overweight sidekick, Jingles?"

"Yeah, I know." I said evenly. "So, do you want me to go tell Dad that I'll do this Saturday chore for you?"

"Of course not, Jingles," he laughed as he skipped out of our bedroom. "It's gotta be something good if you're willing to pass up our favorite Saturday morning Westerns, right?"

"Yeah, I guess so," I said slowly as I followed my brother out to the living room.

"Well, Dennis," said Dad to my brother. "Here's your assignment should you choose to accept it. I know it's Saturday, so you don't have to do it if you don't want to. I think your little brother has some interest, but you're older, so I wanted to give you the first opportunity." Dad was smiling at both of us. He knew that if Dennis had any hesitation before, it vanished at the thought of losing this assignment to his little brother. All three of us understood this particular leverage that Dad used so well.

"OK, now listen closely. You too, Robin, as first alternate." Dad chuckled again. "Mr. Goode has little mutt pups that must be sold this weekend, and here's how we're going to do it." Dad explained his strategy in terms we could understand well, including the part where we kids would split the proceeds with Mr. Goode (we were very excited at this prospect). He also explained that the pups would be drowned in the river if we didn't "succeed". "But don't worry," Dad continued. "If you follow the plan exactly, I promise you every one of these pups will find a good home." (Dad didn't tell Dennis that ours was the safety home. It might have affected our interest in selling the pups he said later.)

The following Saturday morning my brother and I found ourselves on Charlottesville's Main Street strategically placed on the sidewalk between the Victory Shoe Store and the Brass Rail Pool and Beer Hall.

In a nutshell, here was Dad's grand location strategy. It was just two weeks before Christmas and a lot of mothers were going to buy those super $4.95 special Ked's sneakers for their kids at the Victory Shoe Store. While the mothers and kids were shopping at the Victory Shoe Store, often the fathers would go up the block to the Brass Rail for a quick game of pool. They could not miss seeing us as they hurried up the sidewalk to get to Daddy to show him their new holiday shoes. There we were right in the middle of these potential pup buyers.

We stood all dressed up in our grey wool suits with the Knickerbocker shorts, knee socks, grey wool caps and Santa Claus red bow ties. We were finely positioned behind our yellow Coca Cola crate litter of pups. But these were no longer Brownie's ugly pup litter. No. With the magic of a red marker neatly drawn in large lettering on a wooden sign post just above their crate, we had written:

### Genuine Albemarle Beagles
### for Christmas — Only $5.00

I stood next to my brother. Jemima was stretched out behind me. Dad was watching from across the street as my brother did his pitch which he had practiced all week. "Hey, get your famous Albemarle Beagles here. Only five left. Only five dollars. And boy can they hunt. You just won't want to hunt here in Albemarle County without a genuine Albemarle Beagle. Only five left — oops make that four. They make a great Christmas present. But you better get 'em quick cuz they're mighty rare hunting dogs, these genuine Albemarle Beagles, the last ones before Christmas." You get the idea.

I must admit my brother was pretty good at it. I think he enjoyed his role as pitch man almost as much as playing Marshall Matt Dillon. His way of handling the prospects (with a little coaching from Dad) was pretty good too.

"Yes, sir, these really are genuine Albemarle Beagles. In fact they were born about five miles from here in Albemarle County itself." "Pedigree? No, sir, but I hope with the money I raise to go to college one day." "How big will they get? How big would you like them to get?" (A small winsome chuckle followed.) "Oh, yes, sir, they come from champion hunters... Albemarle Coon hunters, I think."

It was a magical performance… and a terrifically successful day in selling the world's newest unofficial dog pedigree, the famous Albemarle Beagle.

By noon on that Saturday, all the pups were sold, the last to a slightly inebriated fellow who had just lurched out of the Brass Rail. He had wanted to know if these Albemarle Beagles were good guard dogs. My brother assured him that if he fed the dog and loved it well, this dog would guard him against almost anything … because, as my brother put it, this was just the nature of the Albemarle Beagle.

Approvingly, our last customer picked up this last pup, which was the runt of the litter, and gave my brother the five dollar purchase price. As he walked away, my brother and I both heard the man talking to his new dog, "OK Rex, I hope you will also guard me against my wife when I come home a little tipsy." (This, as he gave Rex a little scratch under his right ear.)

Everyone seemed pleased that cold, bright December day: the customers, Dad, my brother, Jemima and me (even if we were only used in a support role).

Mr. Johnny B. Goode came over in the evening of that very Saturday to find out how the "ugly pup" sale went. In those days his house did not have a phone so he came in person.

Dad met him at the door with a big grin. "Well, Johnny, with the help of my two boys, we sold every one of those little mutts, right there on Main Street in downtown Charlottesville, sold 'em all by noon today."

"Did you actually sell 'em?" a bemused Johnny B. Goode wanted to know.

"You betcha, Johnny. Young Dennis here was the pitch man and Robin and Jemima here were the support team."

Dad handed Mr. Goode $12.50 in cash and continued, "Yep, we created a whole new breed  – called 'em Albemarle Beagles, and  – hey Johnny, what's the matter with you?"

Mr. Goode was laughing so hard, it looked like he was having trouble breathing. He took off his hat and started slapping his knee with it. He danced a kind of turkey trot, with his feet moving triple time. At last he seemed to recover himself as he tried to answer my Dad, even as he kept chuckling to himself.

"Oh no, Mr. B., I don't believe it. This is the greatest thing that has happened since we moved out to your farm — and the funniest."

"Well, Johnny, share the joke. What's got you laughing like Abbott and Costello?"

"OK, Mr. B., but you're not gonna believe it. You sold those little pups as Albemarle Beagles, right? Well, listen to this. You remember my sister-in-law Helen? A couple of weeks ago I offered to give her one of the litter, and she said they were just ugly little mongrel mutts and she wouldn't have one in her house. Well, this afternoon she came by the house to tell Dorothy, she sure was glad she hadn't settled for one of Brownie's litter, you know, cuz she had just bought herself a genuine Albemarle Beagle — and for only five dollars — oh, that snooty old bag. I tell you Mr. B., it's just too good to be true. Oh wait 'til I see old Helen. I can't wait to tell her."

Mr. Goode started laughing that high mountain hollow sound. Dad slapped him on the back and ushered him toward the front door, all the while advising him that he should go easy on Helen. In fact, he might just want to keep the Albemarle Beagle caper a private joke, or he might end up with an extra Albemarle Beagle back at his house. And this might further upset Mrs. Goode, Dad suggested.

"Hmm, I expect you're right, Mr. B.," said Johnny B. Goode. "Every time I see Helen I won't ask her how that "Genuine Albemarle Beagle" is doing — but I will laugh a little, but only me and Brownie are going to know."

"This is going to be a great Christmas," said Mr. Goode as he strode out the front door with the $12.50 clenched in his hands. "Hey, thank your boys, oh, and you too, Jemima. You're a goodun'. Now, with this money I'm gonna buy that dress from Leggett's that Dorothy has been asking for. With the two dollars left, I could get me a six-pack of Arrow 77." Johnny looked at my Dad one more time and winked. "Nope, I'm gonna go down to Gleason's Saddlery and buy Brownie a brand new red leather collar. I reckon she deserves it." We all watched Mr. Goode saunter off into the night.

Dad turned back to my brother and me with that broad smile still on his face. He gave my brother eight dollars for his good work, and I received $4.50 for Jemima and me. I realized I couldn't buy the three-speed Schwinn bike I'd been longing for with this amount, but it was certainly enough for the Matt Dillon Quick-Draw Holster I'd seen advertised in the Sears and Roebuck catalogue.

If I couldn't have the fastest bike in the neighborhood, maybe I could have the quickest draw just like in Gunsmoke. And, for sure, Jemima would have the prettiest collar.

The very thought of all this made me smile, and that made Jemima wag her tail. She always wagged her tail when she saw me smile. I decided to get her a little extra kibble for her bowl. We headed for the kitchen.

It all was thanks to Brownie and those famous Albemarle Beagles for Christmas, December of 1955.

# THE COURAGE TO UNSTEAL A BELT

It was a week or so after the theft. I felt guilty and alone. I felt like a piece of ham hung out to dry at the local butcher, twisting ever so slowly while everybody passed me by. My older brother, Dennis, had developed a group of friends at the Kanawha County Pool where he went each day to play Marco Polo, eat ice cream sandwiches, and stare at the girls. My friend Donny and his brother R.A. had joined a swim team and left every day at five a.m. for practice, in preparation for all those summer meets. They were gone all day so I hadn't seen much of them in a while.

One day I went with Fred Dudley, my backyard neighbor and fellow club member, up to Shadwell's Drug Store. We sat at the soda fountain and drank Cherry Cokes and ate two bags of Sugar Babies. I was feeling a little better until Fred asked me why I wasn't wearing that cool alligator belt Donny told him I had stolen from Leggett's last week. Fred gave me a conspiratorial wink, as if we had shared a great rite of passage. Now I felt even more depressed.

I dropped my head as if to examine some old gum attached to the base of my stool. Then I stood and told Fred that I had forgotten to "finish some stuff" at home. I left him looking vaguely hurt as I rushed out the door. I did have chores to do when I got home but the fact is, I realized in that moment that I didn't want to talk to anyone about the belt or anything else.

Since it was summer, Dad had assigned me a few extra chores around the house, like mowing the lawn and washing the cars — something different each day "for a little extra money. It'll keep you out of trouble," he said. Did he know something? Nah.

Well, I guess the chores did keep me busy, but they didn't keep me from feeling sad and blue — "lower than a snake's belly," as I heard Dad describe one of his post-party hangovers. I was depressed from the moment I woke up in the morning to the moment I collapsed into bed at night, and I just couldn't shake it. Depression is very tiring, apart from everything else. You feel like you're walking through glue to go anywhere, to do anything, even to *think* anything. All you can manage are vague recurring thoughts that something bad happened or is happening to you, and you can't do anything about it.

I would fall into bed at night and stare at the ceiling above me, trying to figure it all out before finally drifting off to sleep. I mean, why was I, a perfectly good, pretty smart, pretty athletic twelve-year-old, unable to shake these blues? I knew that leaving Charlottesville and all my lifelong friends was a shock, but I had made new friends in Richmond. They were a little different from my Charlottesville friends but they were good guys and I liked them a lot. Was I feeling blue at the realization that my best friend Jemima had gotten old and would one day soon leave me forever? Death can be such an injustice. It's a pretty depressing concept for a twelve-year-old to contemplate.

I knew, though, there was something more. It was *me*. I had changed, and I really didn't like the new me, not at all.

"Hey, Robin!" It was my brother. "Get up and get dressed. Mom's going to drive us over to the pool right after breakfast. I think we're gonna stay all day." It was the thirteenth day after the heist.

"Nah, I think I'll just hang around here," I said. "I've got stuff to do."

"Like what? Lying in bed and picking your nose? Hey, come on. What's the matter? Something's bugging you, isn't it?" Looking back, I think my brother was actually worried about me.

"Nah, I'm just tired," I said. "Hey, thanks anyway. I'll see you when you get back."

"OK, Tonto," said my brother. "But if you want to talk about something, if you're feeling bad about something, you can always talk to me …well, you know what I mean."

"Yeah. Thanks." I watched as my brother left my bedroom. I proceeded to toss a little rubber ball up to the ceiling and catch it as it popped back into my hands. *I had done this thousands of times in the last week or so; I was looking for an answer.*

Then I hit upon it. It wasn't the moving, growing up, growing old, or even death and dying that really depressed me. I knew I had no control over those things. In time I knew I would adjust to the life issues that confront everyone. These were simply a couple of the more disagreeable aspects of life and I knew in time I would somehow learn to handle them.

The uncontrollable bad stuff wasn't at the root of my depression, but the controllable bad stuff sure was. It was all about that ugly simulated-leather alligator belt I had stolen last week. Stealing it was wrong on every level, and the fact that I'd done it as a club initiation rite was certainly no excuse. I should have been strong enough not to let a bunch of guys talk me into it even if it meant I wouldn't get into the Spring Drive Treehouse Club if I didn't steal it. I knew I couldn't talk to my father about it. I couldn't even talk to my brother. What would I say? I was too ashamed.

I threw the little rubber ball up to the ceiling again, and it came down too hard. It rocketed through my hands and smacked me in the nose. "Ow!" I yelled. "Geez, I can't even catch a stupid ball." I felt sorry for myself, and then I hated myself for feeling sorry for myself. That old favorite, vicious cycle. You get the picture.

"Wait," I said out loud, to no one in particular. "There *is* something I *can* do." I jumped out of bed and paced up and down my room. The solution to the seemingly unsolvable problem began to emerge. I would simply *undo* the theft. I would thereby recover my self-worth by doing something even scarier than when I first stole that ugly alligator belt. I would put on that alligator belt and ride my bike back to Willow Lawn, go into Leggett's, head for the belt section, take the belt off, and rehang it on its original rack. I knew that if they caught me actually putting the belt back, they'd probably accuse me of stealing it, and that would be pretty hard to explain:

"Uh, sir, I was simply returning a previously stolen belt so that I could unsteal it."

Right.

"Okay," I said, standing there in my room. "My mind is made up. I'm going to do this while I still have the nerve." I walked to the closet and opened the door. I swear I could still see that alligator buckle gleaming up at me from the darkest corner of the closet … even though I thought I'd thrown some dirty laundry over it.

I reached down, grabbed the belt and threw it on my bed. I put on my Mickey Mantle T-shirt and some blue jeans and laced the alligator belt through its loops. Boy, did I hate that belt! I had to follow my plan before I lost my nerve. I ran down the stairs, through the side door, and into the garage. I hopped on my bike and headed out for Willow Lawn. I felt a little like the Lone Ranger. I was on a bicyclist's crusade to save the thieving soul of a twelve-year-old.

I rode my bike along Monument Avenue and headed for my *Showdown at Willow Lawn Shopping Center.* I was scared but I knew it was the right thing to do. For the first time in what seemed like forever, I felt good about *something...* even exhilarated.

I hopped off my bike and slid it under the giant cedar tree at the entrance to the shopping center, just as Donny and I had done the previous week. I walked quickly toward Leggett's, the store where I'd committed my crime. I looked at the hours of operation that were posted on the glass door: ten a.m. to six p.m. I looked at the Roy Rogers watch my mother had given me for my birthday a couple of years before – nine fifty-five.

I walked quickly away from the store. Was it guilt or fear that created this overwhelming tightness in the pit of my stomach? No, I realized, I had cinched the belt too tight. I smiled a little as I loosened the buckle. I walked to the edge of the shopping center's parking lot, next to Monument Avenue. I thought about heading back to the cedar tree, jumping on my bike, and going home when I noticed a church billboard next to the road. It read: *More than a shopping bargain – Here you can save your soul.*

As a five-finger discount item, the stolen alligator belt was certainly a shopping bargain, and I did feel it had cost me my soul – a soul I could not save unless I completed my unstealing campaign.

I turned around and walked slowly back toward Leggett's. I sensed the heat rising up from the concrete sidewalk beneath my feet and I felt the morning sun beating down on my back. Somewhere I heard a clock chime ten times. I found myself at the Leggett's door again. I watched the security guard unlock the big glass doors and push them open.

"Coming in, kid?" he asked, as he held the door wide open. "You must be here for that special on the Mickey Mantle Homerun sneakers, right?"

"Uh, right," I said as I edged past him.

"Well, you better hurry on up to the third floor. We've only got a few pair left."

I took the elevator to the third floor, the home of Mickey Mantle shoes and the awful alligator belts. Then, I eased on over to the belt section, and found the very hook from which I had stolen the ugly alligator belt. I noticed there were six more identical belts hanging from the same rack. Obviously, a big seller.

I looked around. Everyone seemed otherwise occupied. I unclipped the belt, quickly pulled it through the loops of my jeans, and hung it back on its hook.

That was it. Done. Again, I look around. Nothing. I quickly walked to the elevator and took it down to the main floor. Then I eased back toward the entranceway and the beckoning glass doors. Just like that, I was standing outside in the bright sunshine. I felt great. The blues were lifting, and life was starting to feel good again. I took a deep breath and smiled.

Then I felt a tap on my shoulder. "Hey, kid, where are you goin'?" I turned to face the security guard.

My heart began beating fast. Blood rushed to my cheeks. *Red cheeks of guilt. Worse than that, telltale cheeks of fear and guilt.*

My feet were frozen in place. I waited to be apprehended. It was just like the popular TV series Dragnet, in which Jack Webb would catch the bad guy just when he thought he had gotten away with it.

"What's the matter, kid? You look a little hot. I just wanted to ask you if you found those Mickey Mantle sneakers you were looking for."

"Uh, no," I began. "I decided they were too expensive." *Maybe I'm not going to get caught, I thought to myself.*

"Hey kid, what happened to your belt? I could have sworn you had one on when you came in. I remember 'cuz there was a cute little alligator on the buckle."

"Oh, no," I said, perhaps too quickly and too loudly. "Uh, no, I didn't put on a belt this morning."

"Hmm, are you sure?"

"Oh, yes, I'm sure. I don't like wearing belts. In fact, I really hate belts."

"Well, okay," said my friend the security guard, ever so slowly, "but next time, wear tighter jeans. The ones you've got on are about to fall down to your knees. See ya, Droopy Drawers." He laughed and walked back into the store. Then he looked back through the big glass doors and winked at me.

I hitched up my jeans once more and walked away fast, but not too fast. I didn't want him to think I was running away from something. It might look suspicious. I headed to the cedar tree and biked out of the parking lot to Monument Avenue. From there, I pedaled fast to Spring Drive and home.

When I got home, our house was strangely quiet. I parked my bike under the volunteer shade tree that marked the border between our yard and Donny Elmore's. I knocked down the kickstand with my left foot, turned, and slowly looked around. Neither Donny nor R.A. appeared to be around. *They must be off at swim practice*, I thought. In the distance I could barely make out the club tree house, the source of my previous thievery initiation rites for which I had just atoned.

I chuckled to myself as I hooked my fingers through the empty belt loops on my jeans. The ordeal was over, and maybe I'd learned something good about myself. I was still mulling this over as I turned from my bike and walked towards our house.

The garage was open and empty, which meant Dad was still at the university, and Mom and my brother were probably still at the Kanawha Pool. I was alone and glad to be so. I hitched up my beltless jeans for the umpteenth time, and sat on our porch steps, looking out once more on the world with which I had so recently been confounded.

Just then I heard three tentative scratches on the front door screen. In those days no one ever thought of locking up on a hot summer day; our screen doors kept the bugs out and the occasional dog in.

Jemima stood looking out at me, shaking her Louis Quatorze ears slowly and wagging her stub tail. Having made eye contact, she emitted a short, raspy, insistent bark. Jemima's voice had gotten a little muffled over the past twelve years, but her message was clear: "I'm ready to come out. After I inspect the rhododendrons by your bicycle, I'd like to come back and sit by your side," or something like that. After twelve years together, one raspy bark could say a lot.

I opened the screen door. Jemima passed me with a grateful glance as she padded off past my bike and into the bushes. She moved briskly, if not swiftly, and with determination. "Old age and arthritis," my Mom had said. "Don't worry, as long as she's happy, we're happy." Whatever *that* meant.

Jemima returned from her urgent task. *Better here than on my bed,* I thought. either way, it was okay with me.

I was grateful for her company. I watched her sagging liver-and-white body as she worked her way up the porch steps and sat next to me, close enough that I could feel her warmth. She sat on her haunches looking out, as if trying to see what I was seeing. Then she turned and gave me a small lick on the cheek. She settled down on all fours, pressing herself against me. She breathed a sigh of satisfaction as I scratched behind her ears and massaged her neck with quick, light hand grabs along the ridge of her body, down and back up again. In less than a minute, Jemima was asleep, and I was alone again with my thoughts. But not really. I could still feel her warmth and I could feel her spirit; in fact, I can feel her spirit as I write this now.

At that moment, though, with Jemima sleeping quietly by my side, I thought about other things, some of which I had long ago repressed in my subconscious. Others were new thoughts, triggered by everything that had happened to me in Richmond.

One thing I knew: things were never going to be the same. I remembered all the times my parents had said, "When you get older you can do this or that," or "When you grow up you can make your own decisions."

*Fair enough,* I had thought at the time. *I don't want to grow up anyway. I've got the Order of the Marble, the gang, Wild Bill Hickok and shots of Kool-Aid with my brother in our bedroom, and, of course, I have Jemima. In fact, I believed at the time that I would have been quite happy to go to Never-Never Land with Joer Pan, Wendy, and Jemima, and never grow up. As for all the freedom and responsibility that would come with growing up, include me out.*

But it was not to be, I realized, as I sat there on the front steps with Jemima. The process of growing up is not a choice; it happens to you whether you are ready or not.

And now I realize that it was not so much my life in Charlottesville that was over. It was my childhood itself that was nearing an end.

Just then the old black Chrysler convertible, top down, turned into our driveway. Mom had on one of those broad-brimmed straw hats secured by a string tied loosely around her chin. She smiled into the sun as only she could. In the back seat, pressed against the fading red leather, was my brother. He had a squirt gun in his hands and he was firing it at the back of a boy I didn't recognize. I could see they were all smiling as I felt the remains of this hot blue-sky day starting to fade.

"Hello, Robin," Mom sang out cheerily as she got out of the Chrysler and spotted me across the lawn. "Did you have a good day?"

"Uh, hi, Mom," I replied. "Let's just say I had an interesting day." I paused briefly, and then added, "I guess it was a good day."

"Good," said Mom, sidestepping her way past Jemima and me on the porch stoop. "I've got to go inside and start dinner for your father. He should be home any minute. Oh, by the way." I could still hear her voice as she trailed off towards the kitchen. "What did you get up to today?"

"Uh, nothing much."

About this time my brother literally jumped out of the back seat and onto the ground, as did his new friend. They headed my way, still squirting each other. As my brother approached, he very accurately plugged me and then Jemima, still at my side.

I smiled vaguely at my brother, who was giggling and pointing at us, his hapless victims. I knew he was showing off for his new friend, so I really didn't mind. Jemima, however, startled awake by wet spray and noise, rose up on all fours, bared her teeth, and growled ominously. Dennis immediately stopped his water gun campaign. "Easy, girl, easy now. Hey, Robin, tell your dumb dog we were just kiddin' around."

I gave Jemima a calming pat. "Relax, girl, he didn't mean to startle you, did you, Dennis?"

"Uh, no," my brother agreed, backing up slightly while keeping a wary eye on Jemima.

Jemima stopped growling and pressed herself firmly against my side, but her eyes never left my brother and his new friend.

This was not all bad.

"Hey, Squirt," said my brother with a grin, "this is my friend Tommy

Herbert. We had a cool time at the pool, and his mother said he could have dinner with us tonight and guess what…he lives right here in Spotswood Park, just three streets over! This is so cool." Dennis turned to Tommy. "Hey, let's go inside and get some Kool-Aid. Then we can play ping-pong on the side porch." My brother stepped past me on the side opposite Jemima and entered the house. Tommy followed close behind.

"Hi, I'm Tommy," he smiled as he passed me. I reached up and managed a quick shake of his outstretched hand before he disappeared inside behind my brother.

*What a nice guy,* I thought. *My brother needs a good friend.*

*I'm lucky,* I thought, *as I scratched behind Jemima's ears. Good days or bad, I always have my best friend. I have Jemima.*

## A BASEBALL STORY

It was the summer of 1957. I had just turned twelve and I remember that week as full of strange emotions. It was as if I were on this invisible passageway out of innocence, out of childhood. I don't remember what started the process, but I began to think differently about my small life, and the larger more forbidding world that surrounded it. It was as if I were a part of it, yet outside looking in. It was all a little scary and sad at the same time, but I realized there was nothing I could do but try to make the best of it.

We had the usual baseball games with R. A. and Donny Elmore, Fred Dudley, Jay Dew and the rest of the gang. After the games, we usually walked over to Shadwell's Drug Store and Fountain where we would have Cherry Cokes and Sugar Babies. We sometimes held club meetings in our tree house, where we coughed our way through Salem Menthol cigarettes that Jay had filched from his mother's purse. But even then, I sensed changes going on in myself, my pals, and the world around us.

Often, R. A. would want to quiz me, right there in our tree house, about American History because he had failed it the previous year and he was afraid he would fail it again this year. Because my Dad was a history professor, R. A. figured I might be able to help him. He wanted desperately to go to college one day, while his brother didn't seem to care at all even though he was a straight-A student. Fred was just a nice guy who knew he was going to be a plumber just like his father before him. And Jay didn't know what he wanted to be when he grew up, and he was suspicious of everyone who did, even his friends.

"Don't worry about your future, Jay," R. A. would say. "You'll probably end up in jail for assault and battery anyway." Everyone would laugh, except for Jay.

We had had one of those mid-afternoon 'Smoke and Talks' in our tree house when Fred broke in. "Hey, let's cut the bull and go have fun. Let's go on over to the church grounds and play some baseball. I'll get a couple more guys from my street, and Donny, why don't you go find Steve Street and Billy Herbert."

"Yeah, good idea," agreed Donny. "I'll bet they're all hanging out at Shadwell's. Let's go."

Twenty minutes later, everyone showed up at the church grounds, and we quickly formed up two teams. I was glad to see Jay Dew was on my team. At least he wouldn't attack me, theoretically, but with Jay you never knew.

The game went quickly, but by the seventh inning our side was ahead by five runs. R. A. had hit a homer with the bases loaded...a grand slam... and even I had knocked in a run with a blooper single just over the second baseman's outstretched glove. Our side was comfortably ahead. Life was good. The other side, somewhat less exuberant, suggested we call the game as they 'had to go to supper' anyway.

"No! Two more innings. That's the rule," said Jay menacingly.

"Whatever," said Donny at his most definitive.

In the meantime, I had been watching this kid who had come to watch us play. In fact he used to watch a lot of our games. He watched because we wouldn't let him play. He never even asked to play. But today we were so far ahead we couldn't possibly lose.

"Can I pinch hit for somebody?" the kid asked.

We knew he would be an automatic out, but it was my turn to bat and we couldn't lose, so I thought, 'why not?'

"OK, kid, you can bat for me," I said. "Hey, what's your name?"

All those games we had played that summer and no one had ever asked him his name. He didn't play. He only came to watch.

"Charlie," he said, with a smile on his face, as he hopped and skipped past me to home plate.

"Hit a homer," I said, knowing it would be almost impossible for him to even make contact with the ball.

I watched him position himself. First, carefully the feet were balanced. Then he dropped his crutches. He was teetering back and forth. That's when I noticed how muscular his arms were, probably the product of doing all the work of pulling his legs along. Then, I saw him cock my bat over his right shoulder as he peered out to Joe Saunders, the other team's pitcher.

The wind up – first pitch – 'Pow!' He really hit it, way out to center field. But he was sprawled in front of the plate. Gradually, laboriously, he began to pick himself up. We began cheering, "Come on, Charlie!"

I picked up his crutches and positioned them under his arms. Charlie pointed his crutches forward and pulled his legs even, as he willed himself towards first base.

All during this time, the ball Charlie had hit, it seemed an eternity before, had soared over the center fielder's head and rolled to the fence. Our base runner, who had been on first base, had passed second, rounded third, and was on his way to score at home plate.

Meanwhile, Charlie fought and dragged himself towards first base, ever so slowly. We were cheering him on, screaming, merging our wills with his. By now the center fielder had retrieved the ball and thrown it to the cut off man, who wheeled and fired it in the direction of first base. Two more swinging hops, six feet, and Charlie would be there.

Suddenly, it was over. 'Whap' went the ball as it smacked into the cradle of the first baseman's glove.

Charlie was out. He hit a ball far enough to be a homerun for any of us, yet he was out before he could reach first base. We were stunned, unbelieving.

Charlie turned around slowly and sought me out with his eyes. Then he hopped over to me. I looked down at the ground. I didn't know what to say. Somehow, his failure was my failure, all of us felt that way.

He was next to me now. Slowly I looked up to see the fire in his eyes.

"Thanks for letting me play. Next time, I'll put it over the fence." Charlie grinned again.

I remember saying to myself, "It isn't fair." We all felt that way.

It was only much later, as I relived those moments, that I understood. Charlie had hit a homerun and was tagged out at first, yet his smile was one of victory. Despite everything, the crutches and the useless legs, and the homerun that became an out, Charlie had done what he had set out to do for so long – *He had played the game*! And for him, at this moment in his life, that was enough.

I said goodbye to Charlie. We shook hands and he smiled at me as he gripped his crutches and headed off. He stopped briefly, turned and said, "Maybe tomorrow."

"Maybe," I smiled back at him.

"Great." He waved a crutch at me, and then began to disappear into the distance.

*Maybe not*, I thought. The other guys might not want to put up with a 'sure out,' who couldn't even field the ball. But we never had to make that decision, because I never saw him again, neither at the ball games or anywhere else. To this day I don't know what happened to him, but I hope I never forget what I learned from Charlie on the church ballfield that day.

Do your best with what you've got in the situation in which you find yourself.

Charlie did not say that about his homerun that became an out. He showed it. He was living it. He was truly playing the Game of Life as it was meant to be.

Thank you, Charlie.

**Adapted from**

*Norton's Lament*

# LOVE IN BLOOM

I remembered that warm spring day in 1966 when I found myself walking briskly towards Randolph Macon Women's College. I was going to get together with Sally Melbourne, a girl I had briefly met at a fraternity party the year before. On a whim, and because I knew virtually no one else from the old days in Lynchburg, I had gotten up the courage to call her, not knowing what we would have in common, given our current relative circumstances. But when I had told her a little bit, about dropping out of W&L and how now I came to find myself in Lynchburg employed as a Trailways ticket agent, working odd hours, she had laughed out loud.

"Well, since you work from 3:00 to 11:00, you can't exactly ask me out for a date, can you?" Melbourne was always direct it seemed.

"Yeah, I guess it is a bit difficult," I said slowly. "I just wanted to say hello."

"Good," said Melbourne. "So why don't you come over for lunch here at the college? We have pretty good food, and for some reason, there are three different cafeterias. This means by rotating, you can come three times a week for a free lunch without appearing to be too much of a freeloader." She laughed again, but it was as if she was sharing the joke with me, but not at my expense. It was as if we were beginning a delicious little conspiracy together, us against the school, us against the world, a conspiracy of gentleness and laughter in which no one was hurt.

"Well, that's great, Melbourne," I said. "The great 'Randy Mac' cafeteria conspiracy begins. I'll start lunch tomorrow…uh, if you're serious."

"Oh, yes, Norton. I'm serious. I've never had a date with a Trailways ticket agent before. You just get over here at high noon tomorrow."

"I'll be there," I had said. "Can I bring anything?"

"No, but I might make you sing for your supper, so to speak."

"What do you have in mind?"

"Oh, I don't know," Melbourne replied. "How about a Cafeteria Callout of all Trailways bus destinations from Lynchburg to New York City?"

"You would have me do this out loud right there in your school cafeteria?"

"I might," she said.

"Well, I welcome the challenge."

"Good, and Norton…"

"Yes."

"Bring me something from the ground. See you tomorrow." Melbourne laughed again and rang off. That was yesterday.

I stepped over yet another sidewalk crack as I walked along. I wanted all the luck the day might bring and I certainly didn't want to 'break my Mother's back'. In my hands were a bunch of six pink primroses, a gift from Mrs. Tompkins, my 81-year old landlady, in thanks for my help in the yard the day before.

"Well, Norton," she had said. "I do believe this is the first time I've seen this kind of fire in your eyes since we met. I'll be guessing it's about that college girl. I couldn't help but hearing you talk with her on the hallway pay phone last night." She had handed me a small bouquet of flowers. "Well, these primroses are from my earliest blooming garden bushes. They're guaranteed to make that girl smile, and that's what you want, isn't it, to make her smile?"

I looked down at the beautiful spring flowers and replied, "Yes, ma'am. They are something from the ground. I think they will do just that …, make her smile."

---

When I reached the circular entrance to Randolph Macon Women's College, I entered through the twin glass doors of the brown limestone building which served as admissions for all visitors. It was dark, almost Gothic in nature. The doors swung open magically, as Melbourne suddenly appeared, with her smile of warmth and welcome and just a hint of mischief. She was quite unmistakable in tight faded blue jeans, her red tennis shoes, and her 1950s style green and yellow searsucker shirt. It was all loose fitting, free flowing, yet still revealing a fit and gently curving figure. She was more beautiful then I remembered. And there was the same chemistry, an indefinable connecting essence. I remember even now that I had felt it in our brief encounter the year before, and I had felt it on the phone the night before, and I felt it even more now.

Although Melbourne never called on me to "make the Trailways calls" during lunch, I probably would have done so with pleasure. Being the only male having lunch with the girls at an all girls' college, I was instantly the center of attention. Darting eyes were always upon me. Secret smiles came from everywhere, and one girl even dropped a note in my lap as she walked by our table. Melbourne laughed as she leaned across the table and reached down into my lap to retrieve it. I enjoyed this too.

"Hold onto your knickers, hot shot, and we'll see what she said." "Hmm," said Melbourne slowly, as she read out loud. "Meet me outside the Grey Dorm at 3 o'clock, and I'll make it worth your while." Melbourne watched me gleefully as this sudden excess of attention seemed to have left me a little embarrassed.

"Don't be too impressed with yourself, sport. The note is from Annie Schultz. She's so horny she tried to make it with the custodian last year. He is 65 and he's black, which would have proven to be an obstacle for some of our more conservative girls. But not Horny Annie. Anyway, Bill, that's the custodian, had the good sense to turn her away and to suggest that the rest of us kind of look out for her. Basically, he was a real good guy about it, but that still left her horny, and then you come along as the noonday sampler. But that's OK. I'll protect you."

With this, Melbourne reached across the table and smiled at me. Her eyes were glistening, and her smile somehow flooded into me with its warmth. It was wonderful and indescribable, except to the other Sisters of Grey Cafeteria. "Uh oh, better leave him alone. That one belongs to Melbourne."

I kind of felt that way too.

*Good Days Sunshine*

It all happened so quickly, infatuation turning to love. For the next ten days, we met every day for lunch. We rotated among the three school cafeterias, and I soon became a kind of mascot for the all-girl student body. Naturally, I didn't mind, and it was apparent to everyone that I did belong to Melbourne. Each day, after lunch, we held hands, wandered around the grounds, and talked about everything and nothing in particular until I had to leave for work. It was magical, as if we had been looking for each other all our lives. Perhaps we had. What I do know is that I was falling in love and all things were possible. I hadn't felt this good since I was a sophomore in high school and made second team junior varsity football. Melbourne was smart and funny and laughed at my jokes, did not judge me, and despite getting offers from lots of guys who were still in college and had a discernable future, for some reason she only had eyes for me. "Thank you, God."

We sat under a Sycamore tree on a particularly warm day in the last week of April. I squeezed her hand and addressed the subject. "Melbourne, you know I'm crazy about you and I'd do anything for you. That's why I don't want you to risk wasting your time with me, when there are lots of guys out there with great futures all laid out who would kill to go out with you."

Melbourne pulled back the hand I was holding and gently slapped me across the face. "You dummy. Do you think I'm looking for the next successful doctor or lawyer or banker? You may or may not become the next Hemingway if that's what you want. But I don't look that far into the future. It's never as clear as it seems and rarely turns out as you hope. I remember when my dad left my mother for another woman, just when I thought I had the perfect family. So don't give me that stuff about wasting my time with you compared to some Econ major at W & L."

Then she put her arms around my neck and pulled me to her even as I could still feel the slap on my cheek. She lightly kissed me, and pulled back. "Norton. All I know for sure is what I feel in my heart." This, as she put my hands on her chest. "I look into your eyes and watch what you do and I feel I know your heart, too. I know your smile, because I make you smile. And you make me laugh, and you make me think, and you make me feel joy. As long as we have that, the future will take care of itself. So stop playing Sidney Carton and kiss me."

"Sidney, who?" I wanted to know.

"Oh, go reread Dickens' *A Tale of Two Cities*. But not now, you dummy," as she pulled me to her. "Right now, I'd like to hold you tight, if you don't mind."

I did not mind. I kissed her and held her tight, as she pulled me down to the ground. I didn't want to lose her. I wanted to stay suspended in the moment, in the warmth of this bright April day with this beautiful girl who held my heart as I held hers.

All of this in the last magical April days of 1966. I had always felt that April was one of the most beautiful months of the year, God's rejuvenation of the grass, of the flowers, and of the trees, all in their triumphant colors, signaling the warmth and renewal of life — a chance to renew your dreams.

But in the back of my mind, other thoughts, old thoughts, and old demons were forming, twisting kaleidoscopally in my brain. For this was also the season which had signaled the beginning of my great depression the year before. I wondered what would happen by May, what would come with the heat of summer? Not only between Melbourne and me, but also what would happen within me.

I knew Melbourne would finish her sophomore year in May, and in keeping with her nature, had volunteered to work as a counselor at a camp for the underprivileged in North Carolina. It was owned by Billy Graham, the evangelist. Melbourne had signed up not because she was religious in an organized kind of way, she wasn't, but because she believed in the camp's stated mission to feed and teach North Carolina's displaced and neglected poor children.

"Don't worry, Norton," she had told me with her wonderful smile. "I'm not gonna become 'Born Again' on you. I just want to do a little pay back for all that I've gotten in my life — notwithstanding having to put up with you," this as she playfully pushed me away from her in the tall grass of the back fields of Randolph Macon Woman's College.

No, I wasn't worried about Melbourne or her possible conversion to one of Billy Graham's disciples at Montreat, North Carolina. She was just as likely to convert some of the 'Born Agains' to a more Jeffersonian deistic faith and good works kind of thing. God knows she had me believing in her. What worried me was not her faith, or her strength, or her commitment to me. What I feared was myself and the return of the 'Black Ass' depression, which seemed to come from nowhere and to last a very long time. I knew my very fear of it could create a self-fulfilling prophecy, and I knew the more I thought about it, the more likely it was to overtake me. It was a recurrent nightmare. And now I was having that nightmare every night. I would awake in a cold sweat, and I kept telling myself that this time it would be different. I had a job. I was free of all those things which weren't me, a school I didn't relate to, a fraternity of false friends, and the unknowingness of my future... at least my immediate future.

Here, in Lynchburg, independent of family, I did have a job which paid the bills and time to figure out what came after that. 'So,' I would say to myself, 'for the first time I am legitimate, I am being true to myself, and I have the most beautiful girl with whom to share the joy of the moment and to trust, to confide my hopes, my fears, and despair, but mostly my joy in feeling free, free and with her...' Still, in the back of my mind lingered a little nagging nameless fear which seemed to say, 'Sure, Norton, enjoy it while you can. I'll always be here and sooner or later I'll come back to you and drown you in an ocean of soothing, numbing, nothingness. You'll give it all up for the Black Dog depression. I'll be back, so just enjoy the moment.'

---

"Hey. What has that great big block of a head of yours got itself around?" said Melbourne. We had been lying under the same old Sycamore tree on the back grounds of the Randy Mac campus.

"You look like something's grabbed you by the throat. I know you better than you think I do, so you might as well come clean."

Melbourne gazed into my eyes. It was as if she were reading my thoughts. "Go on. Spit it out, Norton," Melbourne said. "I will wait all day sitting opposite you in this field until you do. So just take your time."

"Well, I've got to start my shift in two hours," I said weakly.

"OK, I'll wait the two hours and we'll see how long you can stay silent. We'll work on your karma," said Melbourne, "if nothing else."

About three minutes went by without either of us saying another word, just sort of gazing out into the bluesky holding hands, and watching two kids trying to play tennis in the distance. Finally, I said, "How about I go play a little tennis with those boys for a few minutes. When I come back, I'll share with you the secrets of my soul."

"All right, Mr. Coward," said Melbourne. "I'll give you five minutes. Then you come back and tell all." She pushed me away. "And you better be good."

Two young boys, about nine or ten, were playing tennis on an abandoned crack-filled hard court, apparently abandoned by the 'Randy Mac' tennis team who had moved on to newer courts. The net was frayed and holey, and the one tennis ball bouncing over and through the net could have been a Labrador Retriever's slobber reject. The two boys standing across the net from each other with their ancient Jack Kramer racquets were laughing and still trying to make it all work.

"Here comes my Poncho Gonzalez bullet serve," yelled the taller boy gleefully as he threw the ball up and missed it completely and fell down on the court and started laughing. He got up and tried to serve again, this time making contact and dribbling the ball across the net where his brother, it turned out, used his racquet like a golf club, hitting the ball solidly and in an upward trajectory over his brother's head, over the fence behind. I actually caught that old tortured tennis ball as I approached the court.

I stepped across the service line as the boys waited for their ball. Melbourne smiled. I had played a fair amount of tennis in high school, and had even coached some in a summer tennis league. I began working with the boys, who had identified themselves as the O'Malley brothers, Tom and Billy. They were eager for instruction and some friendly adult attention. I positioned Tom, the Tall, as I called him, in the ready position to serve, and Billy, his brother, stood across the net, ready to receive. I stood at the net so that I could explain the fundamentals of serving and receiving.

"OK, Tom, now toss the ball straight over your left shoulder. Hold your racquet even with your shoulder. Let the racquet head drop loosely behind your back, and keep your head up. Watch the ball as you throw it up, then bend your knees and hit up and out." I demonstrated a couple of times as Billy tried to hit the ball back.

"Boy, mister, you sure can hit a nice serve," Tom said.

"You will too, Tom," I said. "OK, Billy. Get back over there and wait for Tom's serve. Keep your racquet back and step into the ball when it comes. OK? Tom, are you ready?"

"Yeah. Hey, what should I call you, mister?"

"Norton."

"OK, Norton. Well, here it comes." Tom dropped his racquet head behind his back and tossed the ball up. He leaned into it with all his might and made solid contact. He hit it hard over the net and it went whistling past Billy. It was long, but it was a good looking serve.

"Wow, that was cool," said Tom.

"Yeah, cool," agreed Billy, giggling again. "You practically took my head off." Then we all laughed, Billy, Tom, and I together, which as any father knows is a great way to teach a sport, enjoying it as you go. A little laughter goes a long way.

Within minutes it seemed, the boys, with some assistance, had held two rallies of considerable length, and each had served successfully into the other's court. "You boys are doing great," I said encouragingly. The boys were thrilled and grinned broadly.

It was at this point that Melbourne appeared next to me on the court. She had slipped off and returned from the school equipment room with two additional racquets. "So," said a smiling Melbourne, "is this guy a great tennis coach or what?"

"Yeah, he's the coolest," said Tom.

"Yeah, he taught us everything," said Billy.

"Well, maybe not everything, boys," said Melbourne, "but pretty good for the first day."

"Hey, let me see if I can serve one to you, Norton," said Melbourne as she took one of the boys' racquets and nonchalantly rambled over to the deuce serving position on the other side of the net. 'Wham,' she hit a rocket to the inside corner of my deuce service box. The ball skidded off into the distance.

"Hey, where'd you learn to play like that?" I said.

"Four years varsity at St. Margaret's on the Eastern Shore of Virginia. It was an all girls' boarding school. No boys, so I took out my frustrations on the tennis courts." Melbourne looked over the net at me. "But now I have you."

We both laughed, and then the boys joined us knowing instinctively that this was something good. It was good for all of us.

"Come on, Billy," said Melbourne. "Let's you and I play a little doubles against Norton and Tom, and see what damage we can do." She bounced the lone, mangy tennis ball. "But next time I'm bringing some newer tennis balls."

And so, for the next thirty minutes, Billy with Melbourne and Tom with me, we rallied and played and laughed until Billy said sadly, "Hey, Tom. We'd better get home if we want to be able to play again tomorrow. That's the deal Mom made with us."

"Hey, thanks a lot you guys," Tom said to Melbourne and me, "'cuz this is the best time Billy and I have ever had playing tennis."

"How long have you been playing tennis?" I asked.

"Oh, this is my second time," said Tom. "I was just teaching my little brother here when you came along."

"Well," I smiled, "it's been good playing with you boys as well. You let me show off for my girlfriend." Tom and Billy giggled, and Melbourne flashed one of her world winning smiles.

Momentarily distracted, I continued. "I can see you boys are natural athletes. But if you two want to get better at this sport, you need to practice as often as you can. You both have a great attitude, and I can see you are two brothers who will always help each other. Some families aren't like that, so don't ever lose it. On those days where you can't practice with each other or with someone else, the best thing you can do is practice hitting the ball against the backboard. That's how you'll really get your rhythm down, and your timing, your eye/hand coordination. You'll make that racquet an extension of your arm and learn how to watch the ball come off your racquet every time."

I continued. "So, Tom, Billy, practice and play every chance you get, watch the better players hit, and learn from them. That's how you'll get good."

"OK, we will," said Billy enthusiastically.

"OK, swell, don't keep your mother waiting." The boys started walking away, waving at us.

"One last thing," I yelled after them.

"What's that Norton?" asked Tom.

"Keep having fun, and keep being good to your brother. Both of you. All through life he will be the best friend you ever had." In that moment I wished that I had had that relationship with my own brother, Hal, a rising senior at the University of Virginia…But that's another story.

Both boys smiled. "We will," they said, and then they disappeared into the distance, swinging their racquets at phantom tennis balls.

"I liked those boys, Norton," said Melbourne, chuckling. "And they sure did like you."

"Yeah, I guess they did," I said, putting my arm around Melbourne.

"I like the way you were with them, and I like the way you are with me." She turned and put her arms around me, pulling me down towards her. She kissed me. I pulled her tight against me. We slipped to the ground. I could feel her whole body under me, her arms around my neck, her heart beating fast against mine. I wanted the moment to last forever. Suddenly, Melbourne touched my face and kissed me fiercely, and rolled away. Then she grabbed me by the hand and we collapsed to the ground again, hand in hand, her back pressed against the ground in the shadow of the towering Sycamore tree. It was a union of souls gently and beautifully sealed in time.

I knew the demons of depression which had attacked me so often in the past would return.

And yes, I did remember Charles Dicken's *Tale of Two Cities*. I did remember Sidney Carton sacrificing himself for the other suitor to the love of his life  —  because he knew she would have a better life with him.

Just as I knew I would have to push Melbourne away from me. I was damaged goods, a man condemned by his demons. I knew she would have a better life without me.

But in this beautiful moment, the demons did not exist as the fiercely passionate love of Melbourne covered me up in her essence.

The demons would return as they always did… but they could never take away my memory of this moment with Melbourne.

## TRAILWAYS DAYS

I had been in Lynchburg for three weeks, and had settled in pretty well. Lenny Breeden, who lived down the hall in our boarding house and shared a bath with me, often left his spare teeth in the enamel soap holder at the head of the tub. Still, I soon became accepting of his absent-mindedness. Lenny was a retired Trailways bus driver who had been quick to befriend me. He was lonely and to a certain extent, so was I. From Lenny, I learned of the ambush tactics of Red Spence, my boss, how he would sneak into the bus station by avoiding the glass window exposing the Fifth Street main entrance.

Apparently Red would avoid being spotted by taking a circuitous route through the back streets to arrive at the rear delivery entrance to Trailways. He would burst through the freight door to surprise any employees who were slackin' on the job or even, God forbid, sleeping in the freight room.

As Lenny put it, "That sumbitch used to fire people on the spot, or at least put 'em on report and dock their pay. I think it's the only joy he gets out of life, since his wife won't give it up no more… if you know what I mean."

Lenny continued with big brother enthusiasm. "Hey, Norton, you need to get in on the 'Red Spence Alert' warning system. One of the outdoor freight handlers always spots Red sneaking into the back parking lot in that black and yellow two tone Ford Fairlane he drives. The outdoor freight guy scurries into the freight room and tells the mail handlers, they pass the word to the ticket agents, who simply go on the loud speakers and announce, 'Red Alert, Red Alert.' Works like a charm. Hell, as I understand it, Red hasn't caught anyone 'goofing off' in two years unless we want him to… It drives him crazy. He can't figure it out and it sure does give the rest of us a lot of pleasure…"

---

I was soon deemed trustworthy by the various employees of Red Spence's Trailways Station. I was willing to work hard, and willing to take advice from the baggage handlers as well as from the head ticket agent. The fact that I knew every word to the Young Rascals' Good Loving ("I asked my family doctor what's ailin me. / He said what you need, all you need, is / Good Lovin") was well received. I was accordingly admitted into the 'Red Spence Alert Conspiracy.'

My final initiation into the sometimes mysterious Fraternity of the Trailways agent had to do with the loudspeaker announcement. I had memorized the station stops on all points north, south, east, and west of Lynchburg, and by my second week, I was ready to give my initial audition. Fred handed me the microphone and I proceeded to belt out the stops on the northbound bus. "Now boarding for Madison, Amherst, Lovingston, Charlottesville, Washington, Baltimore, Philadelphia, Newark, New York, and all points north. Last call. Get aboard please!"

I thought my rendition was clear and loud and enthusiastic. I looked to my fellow ticket agents for some sign of approval. But Fred Bowers had a scowl on his face, while the other agent merely raised an eyebrow and turned his back on me.

"What did I do wrong?" I wanted to know.

Fred put his arm around my shoulder and explained the Trailways ticket agent code of public speaking. "There is an unwritten, but absolute law on making destination announcements," he said looking at me earnestly. "You may remember it from being a passenger. It's true that you're supposed to give good volume and rhythm…, but nobody's supposed to actually 'hear' the individual stops spoken so that they can actually distinguish them, especially the passengers. They're supposed to get that cleared up only when they board the bus and ask the bus driver, 'Did he say this bus goes to Lovingston? I couldn't make that out?' 'That's right, ma'am', says the bus driver. 'Now get aboard and take your seat, please.' This exchange makes the bus driver feel important and it makes the passenger feel reassured. It establishes a kind of unspoken passenger bond and respect for the driver's authority. You messed all that up. Why, a passenger might walk by the driver straight to his seat and the driver won't get any credit at all. So don't mess that up again. Volume, yes, enthusiasm, yes, clarity no. You leave that up to the bus driver. Do you understand what I'm telling you, Norton?"

"I do, Fred. Thanks for clearing that up."

Fred gave me the fish eye, but then smiled and said, "Well, all right then. Welcome aboard."

From then on, whenever I announced the bus departures, I was loud and enthusiastic. I boomed out for all to hear, "Your attention, ladies and gentlemen. Now boarding for...

*MadisonAmherstLovingstonCharlottesvilleWashingtonBaltimorePhiladelphiaNewarkNewYork* (imagine the longest word in the English language, all syllables mashed together), and all points north . . . Get aboard please." No passenger could be completely sure whether I had actually called out their particular stop or not. Of course they would be hesitant to ask me for clarification, afraid they might insult me, so they always asked the bus driver or the baggage handler for this information. Everyone seemed happy with this arrangement, including myself, now considered a full junior partner in the mystical Trailways Ticket Agent unwritten code of operations.

No, really.

### Respite

It was the first three months that I enjoyed the most at the Trailways bus station. I had my favorite music, which was constantly being replayed on the station juke box. There was of course "Good Lovin'" and Wilson Pickett's "In the Midnight Hour," and the Swingin' Medallions' "Double Shot of My Baby's Love." And for the lonely times or the mean times, there was Simon and Garfunkel's "I am a Rock," which reminded me that there were always books and poetry to comfort me, books like Joseph Heller's *Catch 22*, to confirm for me the relative absurdity of life, now being dramatized by the Vietnam War itself. And for poetry, I had William Blake to express and validate my feelings. Of course for me, as it seemed for everyone else but Lyndon Johnson, there was always the master lyric manipulator, the other Dylan, Bob Zimmerman.

I liked my fellow Trailways workers and I actually looked forward to my weekly Naval Reserve meetings in Charlottesville. I knew I was preparing for my near-term future, two years active duty, and that seemed all right. I didn't think much about Vietnam one way or the other. The possibility of getting killed there did not as yet frighten me for some reason, especially since I would in all likelihood be serving on a ship. That, together with holding down a real, regular job at Trailways, provided me, in my own mind, with an acceptable structure in my life.

Now, in Lynchburg, in my little one bedroom apartment, I was staring into my cracked one dollar floor length mirror that I had purchased at Rose's, contemplating my life as a ticket agent for Trailways and remarking to myself that it felt pretty damn good. I had a job, some real friends at work, I was making my own money, and hell, I was living a good life, my life, not the one that someone else had laid out for me (in which I was bound to not quite measure up to all expectations; a constant, built into the original equation, which I only now realize). This was my life, and I was really beginning to enjoy it.

Still, the nagging fear of the return of the black ass depression haunted me. I just could not totally shake free of it.

"Get lost, bogey man," I said to myself as I gazed deep into the mirror. "You're not going to get me this time." I smiled bravely I thought, at myself, as I said out loud to no one but myself, and possibly Lenny next door if he was listening: "I'm really going to make it this time…and I'm gonna do it on my terms."

Well, in the moment that I said it, I really believed it. So I said it every day. And I added something to this daily mantra, which just seemed to develop in my head on its own. I said this every day too. "Pour yourself a smile, and give the world some joy" (Yeah!).

I felt now a renewed self-confidence, a certain willingness, some would say suicidal, to try anything I had feared before, a certain joyful, even manic, desire to question so much that I had taken for granted before. But in that euphoric mood, I felt real joy in being alive, as I never felt before. And I didn't want to lose it, no matter what; I didn't want to go back to that awful fear of emptiness, of feeling totally dead inside. But could I avoid it, and if so, how, since I did not even know what brought it on?

Not unlike the Righteous Brothers who sang of losing "That Loving Feeling," I feared losing that mercurial essence that I must protect against all people and all things who would challenge it. Embrace the joy of life and fight all signs of the depression dragon, for they were everywhere, too. It was daily and it was exhausting; knowing that some indefinable circumstance or group of circumstances could unite to throw me back into the pit of despair. But, in the back of my mind, there was a recurrent, perhaps self-fulfilling prophecy that I couldn't resist it forever, that it was inevitable. So though I would fight the good fight, eventually I was condemned to lose it. Therefore, I must enjoy every good moment, unless and until they were all gone. And what then? I didn't know, but it was the one thing I truly feared: deadness and the return to that all consuming depression that had captured me before. I thought that I would rather face anything than go through that again. It made risk-taking very easy, to die in the moment rather that return to living death. What a concept.

So each morning when I woke up in my small one room Rivermont Avenue apartment, it was a little bit like the Tin Man checking to see if he still had his new heart. I was afraid I might wake up without it, that that feeling of joy would have magically exited my body and soul during the night, and I would be left with that black depression that had covered me up for so long.

I sometimes would think of myself like Ben Gazzara of the popular TV show of the time, Run for Your Life, about a man who is told by his doctor he only has 6 months to live. He is determined to make the most of it.

So was I.

It was about 11:30 p.m. that same day, a warm April night. I had just finished my 3:00-11:00 shift, and, instead of going back to my rooming house to call Melbourne, do a little reading, and go to bed, I had decided first to stop in at the Texas Tavern, where you could buy five greasy mini burgers for $1.00. I was hungry and the price was right. Here, I found Fred Bowers, hunched over a counter stool inhaling a burger and fries. I noted that a few drops of mustard and grease had already found a new home on Fred's generous paunch, a paunch which actually sloped under the Formica counter.

Fred looked up from his task when he caught sight of my reflection in the large rectangular mirror, which hung above the fat-splattered cooking grill. "What the hell are you doing here, Norton? I thought by this time you'd be home calling that college girl you're always talking about." He pointed to the stool next to him, and clapped me on the back as I sat down. Then he shoved an entire Tavern burger into his mouth, bun and all, talking all the while and spitting food bits in my general direction.

Almost in self-defense, I interrupted him. "So Fred, I saw you studying that Marine Corps manual at the Depot, today. You're not thinking of joining up, are you?"

"Hell, yes," said Fred wheeling around on his stool so he could face me head on. He swallowed the remainder of his burger. "I'm 20 years old and I haven't done shit except graduate from high school, and I'm the first member of my family to do that. I want more out of my life than this crappy little ticket agent job. I want to toughen up, and I want to see the world." Fred looked at me earnestly, all thoughts of consuming his next Texas Tavern burger temporarily put on hold. "Look here, Norton, I'm not as dumb as you think. I read Time magazine from cover to cover every week, so I've got a pretty good idea what's going on out there. Look at Vietnam. We've got to stop those goddamn communists before they take over the world over there. I mean you've heard of the 'Domino' theory, haven't you, Norton?"

"You mean one country, then another, falling into the hands of those godless Communists, until one day they control all of Southeast Asia, and before long the whole free world. Is that what you mean?" I said in measured tones.

Fred Bowers eyed me closely to see if I was mocking him. He decided to give me the benefit of the doubt.

"Yeah, that's right, and I believe it. Those fucking Russians and Red Chinese are right behind all those North Vietnamese Gooks and Viet Cong, trying to overthrow the legitimate democratic government of Saigon that America is trying to protect."

This was more than a burger full to swallow, and I decided to take another tack. "Well, Fred, whatever you do, try not to get yourself killed."

"Oh, hell no, Norton, I'm going to be a chef. See, I got a plan. I'm not going to wait for my draft number to come up. I've already talked to my Marine Corps recruiter, and he says if I join up now, he can virtually guarantee my chosen specialty, and I want to learn how to cook, I mean really cook. And hey, no matter what, I'll get plenty to eat." Fred laughed as he stuffed the last of his five burgers whole into his mouth and began talking and chewing again at the same time. I turned slightly away to avoid the visual and physical onslaught, which now resumed.

"See, Norton, cooking stations are always behind any front lines. Hey, you gotta protect the food lines and where the boys go to eat so I know I'm gonna get out with all my skin, and when I get out I'm gonna start a restaurant with all the pay I've saved."

"What kind of restaurant?" I asked mildly.

"Oh, you know, steaks, chops, first-class food for the vet and the working man. I'll know what they want. I'm gonna serve beer from all over and maybe some screw top wine. And Norton, I'm going to have outstanding waitresses."

"That could mean anything," I said slowly.

"Exactly."

I pushed myself up from my stool, and left 3 dollar bills on the counter for a meal I had ordered, but never eaten. I was no longer hungry. I turned to Fred and smiled. "Well, Fred, it sure sounds like a plan. But while you're over there cooking on the front lines, when someone says, 'incoming,' don't forget to duck. I want to be able to come to your restaurant in a couple of years and check out the fine food, and uh, the outstanding waitresses."

I clapped Fred on the back, we both laughed, and I turned and walked out of the restaurant. I headed up Rivermont Avenue towards my boarding house, and began ruminating. The odds of Fred opening a successful restaurant were less than 50/50, about the same that Fred would survive Vietnam not dead and not shot up or at least screwed up. On the other hand, maybe it was his best opportunity to escape a Trailways ticket agent kind of life, which both Fred and I had agreed in an earlier talk was, for both of us, a temporary weigh station in the dance of life.

**Adapted from**

*Killing Time in a Small Southern Town*

## PERSPECTIVES
### *and a Church Service*

***Friday Night Drinks at the Farmington Tap Room.*** Early summer 1962. The news was out all across the many layered social strata of Charlottesville, Virginia. Two white boys were to be tried on charges of the kidnapping, extortion, and felony assault of two black boys. A grand jury had certified the charges and a jury had been selected. Judge Donald Stevens had set the trial to begin at 11 o'clock on the following Monday.

It was expected to last no longer than two days. Such was the normal procedure in Charlottesville in those days. The right to a speedy trial was strictly observed. But the nature of the justice meted out was open to debate. Too often justice was tempered by a man's class and social standing … or race.

At Farmington Country Club, it was the Friday cocktail hour in the cavernous Tap Room where golfers and tennis players gathered to discuss the winners, the losers, and the events of the week in a town they largely controlled.

J.T. Dixley motioned to a Black waiter, "Another Cutty on the rocks, Skippy, and don't overdo the rocks." The two other men sitting at his table laughed agreeably as they too ordered refills. It had been a long week what with those redneck hooligans bringing primal fear and loathing to the surface. J.T. didn't like it for business reasons. He had over 50 Negroes working in his textile plant, in an industry that was falling apart. It was all he could do to keep the white workers confident that they would maintain their place in the pecking order. In fact, without the cheap Negro labor, they would be out of work.

J.T. Dixley reached out for the Cutty Sark refill that Skippy had just placed before him. He picked it up and looked through the prism of his glass. He saw through its distorted view of his own knotty pine table, past his drinking companions across the polished black flagstone floor, past the other pine tables now packed with leaders and leader-makers of Charlottesville society. Farmington, whose very manor house was designed by Thomas Jefferson himself in 1820, and established as Farmington in 1927, was rapidly becoming the epicenter of Charlottesville politics, breeding and money.

J.T. Dixley was not only the owner of the Dixley Textile Mills. He was also president of Dixley Brick and Block, and vice chairman of the board of People's National Bank. He held the control of that very epicenter. He and fellow Farmington member General Samuel S. Cartridge were considered the two most powerful members of the Club and probably of Charlottesville society. And so, as J.T. Dixley swallowed his second scotch on the rocks, he felt anger bubbling up within him, anger about that whole stupid redneck assault on those two Negro boys. It wasn't so much the immorality of it all, or even its inherent injustice, it was about money, money that the stupidity of two redneck teenagers could cost him and his businesses. And J.T. Dixley had little tolerance for stupidity, especially when it cost him money.

One of his tablemates interrupted his musing. "You know, J.T., that Mickey Courage/Billy Sprouse thing has been blown totally out of proportion. Hell, you know what it's like for a young buck on a hot summer night with nothing to do. Those boys were just out to have a little fun. I admit it got a little out of hand. I don't deny that. And they should be held accountable. And yes, I'm sorry they kidnapped and beat up those Negro boys so bad. Must have been the heat of the night and their own stupidity. So, I say send Mickey Courage and Billy Sprouse to reform school for six months, and put 'em on probation for a year after that. But that's enough. And I'll tell you why, J.T. Convicting those boys of kidnapping and assault or any such foolishness will make the Negro community think we're rolling over, that we are cow-towing to 'em. We can't have that. All this integration bull put on us from that Commie Court that Eisenhower has put together. First the school integration, now they want to eat with us in our restaurants. Hell, next thing you know they'll want to go to our movie theatres. Then, they'll think they have the right to join Farmington Country Club. We just can't have it. We've got to send a message through this trial, that they've got to stop pushing. We've got to keep 'em in their place. We didn't have any of this trouble before forced integration. And I think the colored people were happier too. So I say let's stop all of this foolishness right now, before it's too late. We've got to look after the Whites – yes, I mean our rednecks – if we're going to keep it all together. Don't you agree, J.T.?"

J.T. Dixley looked at the long, angular face of Bill Barton, a trustfund baby, who had earned his money the old-fashioned way; he had inherited it. Barton spent most of his productive day on the golf course, or in the Tap Room gossiping. J.T. Dixley stared hard at Bill Barton and said, "What you just said was about as stupid and shortsighted as the absolute stupidity of what those boys did. And it's that stupidity that could blow up your precious society, right in your smug face. Do you know why?"

A now chastened and slightly embarrassed Bill Barton said nothing, preferring to look down at his shiny lace-up cordovans.

The third person at J.T. Dixley's table was Justin Logan, a thirty something up and coming land speculator whose family had moved to Charlottesville in the late 1940s. Logan was undeterred by J.T.'s harsh words for Barton. He leaned his short, wiry frame toward Dixley, his blue eyes twinkling, and, with a voice and a face said to charm ladies over and under 50, responded, "So, J.T., tell me, if we're all so stupid, am I to presume you're not?" he chuckled, as did Barton, but more self-consciously. Logan sat back in his chair for the next move. When there was only a cold silence and a steady stare from J.T. Dixley, Justin Logan restated his case. "So, J.T., will you share your Godly wisdom with us poor incoherent Blue Bloods?"

Logan laughed again, but Bill Barton did not join him. All the tables around him had gone quiet as well. J.T. Dixley stood up as if to address the whole crowd. They all wondered if the great J.T. Dixley was about to speak to them at all or, as Bill Barton feared, leave the room in disgust. Many of those at the surrounding tables had overheard the thrust of Logan's petulant questions to J.T. Dixley. Everyone knew that J.T. was not a man to take even the mildest of insults lightly.

J.T. Dixley's voice pierced the crowded cacophony of the Farmington Country Club. "Before I leave tonight," he said, "I have a few parting words for you self-righteous, so-called, patricians of the South. Those of you who can trace your roots back more than three or four generations will find, for the most part, the Irish underbelly, the Italian W.O.P., the English working class, or the Welch coal miner, as I do. We came here for freedom and opportunity, and to have a better life than that which we left behind."

He continued, "We created our own new pecking order – do you think our reborn culture will free you from what you left behind? I think not. We have already freed the Black sweat laborers. We cannot do without them. And mark my words, gentlemen: separate but equal is not the reward they will accept for their toil. Full assimilation is what they will have. If you want to fight it in your mills and your banks, your manufacturing plants, fine. Not me. I'm a realist, not an idealist, and not a bigot.

"I believe they work better for me when I let them have their share, their integrated place in my mills. Fight it if you will, make jokes and snide remarks about your nobility and the lesserness of your colored neighbor. I say your plants will flounder with Black worker infighting, picketing, layoffs, and the like. Meanwhile, mine will thrive. I will embrace the chance because I know it is inevitable. I will make money on it and one day soon I will be pleased to sit right here with you and with my colored superintendent as the new member of good, old Farmington Country Club."

With this, J.T. Dixley tapped the empty chair next to Barry Van Supleworth III. "Right next to you Barry. Soon, my colored superintendent will be your newest club member. And he'll be sitting right next to you, drinking his gin martini."

With that and a short staccato laugh, J.T. Dixley walked out of the Tap Room, leaving those behind him to contemplate his words.

"I'll tell you one thing, Harvey." said Charles Van Horn Jr. to his golfing partner sitting next to him, "These people can work in my mill, but they'll never go to school with my son at Episcopal High School, even if they have pushed their way into our public schools. And they sure as hell are not going to join me at Farmington Country Club unless they want to be a cook in the kitchen or a waiter on the floor or a caddy on the golf course. Right, Jerry?"

Jerry Weinstein, in fact the newest member of Farmington and president of Citizen's Bank which held loans for many of the members of Farmington, paused for a moment and said with a twinkle in his eye, "I don't know, Chuck. We let you in. I would have preferred another pal from the synagogue instead of just one more white Anglo-Saxon Protestant."

There was a silence followed by nervous laughter as the assembled members of Farmington Country Club Tap Room grasped the irony of this last remark.

"Yeah, why did we let Chuck in?" said Joe Pace of table no. 3.

More laughter, except for Chuck, who remained silent. The status quo *would* be preserved.

---

***Friday Night at the Riverside Grill.*** There had been lots of talk of the two White boys who had been charged with assault and kidnapping of two Black boys… but that was not to be the discussion tonight. This was Friday night at the Riverside Grill and that meant a night of celebration. Present were cement truck drivers and finish carpenters, brick masons and mill workers, house painters and plumbers; all stood elbow to arm pit at the long U-shaped bar. They too were celebrating the end of a long work week on this crowded Friday night. They were drinking their long neck Budweiser or Pabst Blue Ribbon, the occasional boiler maker and Ballantine Ale. There were even a few Pepsi drinkers, for Charlottesville was a Pepsi town, but not usually on a Friday night. If the Farmington crowd were the makers and shakers in Charlottesville, then these men were the fuel that drove its work engine. Here in July 1962, where this little bar tavern overlooked the Rivanna River at the dividing point of city and county, the grill was never cleaned, only scraped in order to preserve a unique flavor where the flames would envelop the hot dogs and hamburgers alike, a flavor that was a mix of the past and the present. When your hamburger arrived, charred on the outside, rare on the inside, on a paper plate with homegrown tomato slices and onions, and crowded with a "mess" of French fries, ketchup, mustard, mayonnaise on the side, you knew you were a part of the Riverside Experience on a Friday night.

Friday was also payday, a time when this hard working, hard living crowd was at its loudest, rowdiest, and most jovial. But tonight, there was an undertone of fear, anger, and concern in this all white, all male working class establishment. The Billy Sprouse/Mickey Courage mess bothered them. No Negro had ever tried to be served here, and that's the way they liked it. After all, everyone had their own place. This is how they thought at the Riverside. The Negroes had Vinegar Hill in town and Brenwanna just on the edge of town near the twin lakes. There they could party and dance and drink as much as they wanted. Just do it at their places, like we do at ours. This white working class was OK with separate but equal. Many of them worked with the Negroes during the day, and for the most part everybody got along fine, as long as everyone stayed with their own kind at night. The Riverside crowd didn't much like the forced school integration that had started just a few years before. In fact, they had resisted it with basement schools and private White schools if they could afford it. But after school integration had been bitterly accepted as a fact of life, they were now living with it okay. Some of the Negroes they knew from work were good people, and some of their kids were very good athletes. Integration had produced a better football team, and nothing brought the town together like a good football team.

So the Riverside crowd had come to terms with school integration. Sort of. Some even embraced it. But few wanted to share their after work watering holes, the last bastion against disapproving wives and the Negro who threatened to push by him on the pecking order of life.

Standing at the bar, Joe Dykstra, a plumber, turned to his friend, Bill Fallow, and observed, "You know, Bill, those guys at Farmington, mostly our bosses, don't give a damn what the Negroes do, as long as they keep working and don't riot. Well, I don't care either, as long as they don't push into our neighborhoods, our pools, and our bars. They got their own, for God's sake."

---

***Saturday Afternoon Office Visitor.*** It was now two o'clock on a hot Saturday afternoon at the office of Charlottesville's youngest commonwealth attorney Jack Forester. *I don't even want to know what the temperature is,* thought Jack, as he completed the three-block walk to his office, and unlocked the door. He silently thanked Alice for leaving the air-conditioning on when she had left earlier that day. He grabbed the three messages on her desk she had taken for him that morning, and moved into his office, closing the door behind him. He sat down at his old maple desk and began making notes on Monday's upcoming trial. He began with his statement of charges and his opening statement, all the while wondering if Mickey Courage would break away from Joe Smiley's grip, and agree to his terms for the plea bargain. Jack already knew that Smiley would push his clients to go to trial by convincing them that he could defeat all charges the State had put against them. Would Mickey and his father break from Smiley's grasp and take the plea? And would Billy refuse the plea and roll the dice? Somewhere during these musings, Jack put his head down on his desk to rest *just for a moment.*

He was awakened by a loud knocking on the front door. He sat up, looked at his watch, and noticed he had been asleep for nearly 2 hours. It was 4 o'clock.

Jack quickly got up, went through his door past Alice's desk, and opened the door to the outside. A frail looking Black man about 55 with salt and pepper, curly hair and a small goatee, was staring up at him. He was leaning on a cane and holding what looked to be an old Bill Hogan golf cap.

"Are you Mr. Jack Forester?" he said in a raspy baritone voice, unlikely to come from such a small frame.

"Yes, I am," said Jack softly as he stood in the doorway looking out at the man.

"Well, I am Joseph L. Johnson. I'd like to talk to you about my boy. Will you hear me?"

It was a kind of proud pleading, and Jack could see Mr. Johnson's eyes start to glisten.

"Of course," said Jack. "I know you made a 4:00 appointment through my secretary. Please step into my office and we'll talk." Jack ushered Mr. Johnson back into his office and sat him down across from his desk. Jack could see the sweat pushing through the fiber of his blue tee shirt. It had written on its pocket with two crossed clubs, "Farmington Country Club."

"Mr. Johnson, it's a hot day and all I have in my refrigerator is water and beer. May I offer you something?"

Mr. Johnson looked up from his chair where he had crooked his cane on one arm and settled his flat hat on top of the cane. He was leaning on the arm of the chair as if to catch his breath.

"What are you having, Mr. Forester?"

"Why I believe I'll have a beer," said Jack walking to the small 3 by 5 executive refrigerator that was sitting on a table behind his desk. He opened the door. "How about you, Mr. Johnson?"

There was a silence followed by the same slightly raspy, rich baritone voice. "Well, my wife Jessie, would want me to have water, but she's not here and I don't want our commonwealth attorney to drink alone, it being Saturday and all. Why, I believe I'll have a beer, too."

Both men laughed a little as Jack brought Mr. Johnson his beer and sat down behind his desk with his own. Jack felt some of the tension leave the man's face as he saluted Jack with the beer and proceeded to take a long swig. He put the beer down on the right arm of his chair and looked up at Jack. "You know, Mr. Forester, I haven't had a drink in five years… doctor's orders… Jessie's too. Ever since I got emphysema. My only son got kidnapped and almost beat to death by two white boys. He was a starting junior varsity halfback at Burley, only 16… and now he can barely walk. Oh, he was fast and he was smart too. Almost straight A's. We hoped he might go to college on a football scholarship, first ever in our family. Now all that's gone. He's such a good boy. He loves everybody. He didn't have nothing against those White boys. Why'd they have to hurt him like that?"

There was a pause, then Mr. Johnson continued, "Mr. Forester, this is a small town and even the walls have ears. God knows the city jail does. I hear the Defense is going to try and make my son out to be a homosexual who was trying to come on to those White boys and that's why they did those awful things to him. Well, if he had been, I would have loved him just the same. But I know he wasn't no male prostitute. He was always crazy about girls."

Then Joe Johnson changed his tone. "Mr. Forester, I want to know, are you going to let those White punks who attacked my son…are you going to let them slander him and beat him half to death and walk away free, or will you get justice for me and his family and for my boy?"

"I'm gonna get you justice, Mr. Johnson," said Jack.

"White men's justice?"

"All men's justice," said Jack.

Joe Johnson took another long swig of his beer and stood up. "Well, I'd better get home. Jessie and my girls will be wondering where I went."

"Mr. Johnson, may I offer you a ride home?" Jack knew he could borrow Sheriff's Bredlo's jeep and he wanted to offer something more to the proud man standing in front of him.

"No, thank you," said Joe Johnson as Jack walked him to the door. "If I can still lug around a White man's golf clubs, I guess I can walk me home. But there is one thing you can do."

"What's that?" said Jack.

"You can speak to my people at Ebenezer Baptist Church tomorrow. Tell 'em you really do represent all the people. Tell 'em you're going to get justice for my son."

"What time do you want me to be there?" asked Jack.

"I'll tell Reverend Turner you'll be there to speak at 10:30."

"I'll be there."

Joe Johnson shook Jack's outstretched hand, tipped his hat, and walked out the door. He turned around one more time. "Don't let us down, Mr. Forester. We're mighty tired of disappointment."

## Ebenezer Baptist Church
*Talking from the Pulpit*

Jack looked down from the pulpit of Ebenezer Baptist Church. He had been introduced as the commonwealth's attorney and "the man who says he will get us justice in the Lucius Johnson kidnapping case." Jack felt eyes looking back, reflecting a different viewpoint, some encouraging, some curious, and a large contingent of hostile eyes. Jack felt the coldness.

After all, he thought, these people have experienced a lot of 'White Man's Justice' in the past, imperfect at best, and in many cases for the colored man there had been precious little justice at all.

Jack stood still. He looked out on the congregation once more, gazed down at his notes, then cast them aside and looked up. He knew what he wanted to say to these people. He had been thinking about it long before the Lucius Johnson felony assault/kidnapping affair.

"Thank you for letting me speak to you this morning," Jack began. "I've often heard you singing from across the street, but I take it as a real privilege to hear your voices and see your faces from inside Ebenezer Baptist Church."

There was a murmur of approval and some appreciative smiles at this beginning. Still Jack felt the coldness, suspicion of him and his brand of justice. And who could blame them, what with the Klu Klux Klan marching just outside with the apparent approval of Albemarle Country's own Sheriff Barry Bredlo. Jack decided to address that issue head on.

"What you see outside," said Jack pointing to the church doors, "as odious as it may seem, is freedom of expression. As long as those 'Klanners' are orderly and don't interfere with you or your business, and they have secured their marching permit, they have a right to be out there."

The church went quiet. The silence and the hostility were palpable.

"But, that's why I'm here," Jack continued, "to tell you that if <u>you</u> want to march in front of the court house tomorrow or every day of the trial, you have that right, too. Some White people might not like it, but it is your right, and I'm here today to tell you that your rights will be respected and they will be protected."

"As for securing justice for Lucius Johnson and his family, we have the evidence and we have the corroboration, to prove kidnapping and felony assault.  I want you to understand that the defense will raise false issues in order to confuse or even prejudice the jury against the victim. That, too, is their legal right. They will try by any means available, ethical or not, to prove not that their client is somehow innocent of the charges, for they know they cannot prove that… because he is not.  What they will hope to do instead is to create a cloud around our case in order to prevent us from proving it beyond, and I emphasize *beyond*, a reasonable doubt. Their goal is to sufficiently confuse or prejudice the jury so that at least one if not more will refuse to find the defendant guilty beyond a reasonable doubt."

"Let me make it clear to you how the court system works," Jack continued. "If one or more jurors refuses to join in a guilty plea, and the deadlock cannot be broken, then we will have what is called a 'hung jury.' If that were to happen, the defense probably thinks we won't pursue it, or that we will accept a plea to a much reduced charge such as simple assault and false imprisonment. I want you to know that it is my firm intent to win this case with the current charges and bring home a verdict of guilty on all counts.  But juries and judges can be unpredictable. I promise you that, if for any reason these charges are dismissed, or in the event we get a 'hung jury', I will proceed immediately to refile the charges. I will not let Mr. Billy

Sprouse or Mickey Courage escape the justice and the punishment they deserve."

Jack again looked out on the sea of Black faces. He saw consternation and anger. Could White boys who kidnapped and assaulted two Black boys be really found guilty of these charges in court? Or would it be the traditional White man's justice where they get off with a slap on the wrist?

The anger in this church was palpable, and Jack understood it. He looked down at this sea of anger and continued, "I promise to you that there will be justice for Lucius Johnson. We will convict those White boys of felony kidnapping and felony assault, and I assure you they will go away for a long, long time."

"As your commonwealth's attorney, I will not rest until they are convicted and locked away from society. I know you have not always seen justice in the past. I am here this morning to assure you that in this case you will have justice. I promise you that you will triumph in the end. We will have justice for Lucius Johnson and his family. This I promise you.

"I ask for your prayers and support."

With that, Jack smiled, stepped down from the pulpit and walked down the aisle, past the watchful eyes, yet he felt a sense of relief because he now sensed that many in the congregation believed that he, Jack Forester, would do the right thing. As he pushed open the door to the hot July sunshine, he felt that he had accomplished what he had set out to do at Ebenezer Baptist Church this morning. He had brought a measure of hope and faith that real justice would be served. Now he hoped mightily that he could, in fact, deliver that justice.

As the Church door closed slowly behind him, he heard Reverend Alvin Edwards' invocation. "Let us pray for Mr. Forester and for justice. Amen."

## A TENNIS MORNING

It was about 7:45 Saturday morning, July 21, 1962, as Jack slowly drove his black 1951 Chrysler convertible down Farmington Drive. The white canvas top was down and the southwesterly breeze was still agreeable. The heat of the day had not yet arrived.

Jack patted the back of the red leather of his forward passenger seat. "Come on, Jack. Time to do your duty."

First the coal-black eyes appeared. Then the rest, a large, mostly black, mostly Labrador retriever leapt over the back seat and into the front passenger seat. His tail began wagging fiercely against the arm rest, as he leaned over to give his master a big lick.

"All right, stop it, Jack. It's bad enough we have to share the same name…Oh, all right." Jack the man received a few more wet licks as he reached out and scratched Jack the dog behind the ears. Then Jack the man pulled back his hand and turned down Tennis Lane. The other Jack barked as if in recognition that the pleasantries were over and now began the serious business of guarding the car while his master was off hitting a rubber ball with a wooden stick with a rounded head and a net in the middle of it. No doubt the game would have been better without the stick or the net. Still Jack the dog understood that this was what men did. It was a mystery, but it seemed to give them pleasure so Jack the dog was OK with it.

"All right, Jack," said Jack getting out of the car. "Here's our special shady spot. You guard the car. It's OK to nap occasionally. I'll be back in about an hour and a half." Jack the dog locked his eyes on his master to acknowledge that he understood his job.

Meanwhile, Jack the man walked away and through the giant box hedges and towards Court #5 of Farmington's famous red clay courts, acknowledging to himself that he had a better understanding and warmer relationship with Jack the dog than anyone else. Certainly more so than with his ex-wife of five years who had given him Jack after the first four years of marriage. "I've named him Jack to remind me of your better nature; you know, loving, feeling, and amusing; so even when I have to put up with serious, preoccupied Mr. Lawyer, as least I am reminded of your better side."

"What about the kids," Jack had reacted. "Won't they be a little confused about the name?"

"Oh no darling. Both Henry and Julia will know the difference between Jack the daddy and Jack the dog. Jack's all play and no work. Daddy's all work and no play."

"God," thought Jack as he nodded at his early morning doubles partner. Eight years later and five years divorced, he wondered if his ex had been right. Henry's eleven and Julia's nine. I get to see them once a week and two weeks in the summer if it doesn't conflict with their mother's schedule or mine. I hardly know them. All I know is Jack the dog – have I really been consumed by my work?

"Hey, Jack, wake up, boy. We've got a tough match this morning." It was Jay Cutler, Jack's weekly doubles partner. They had known each other since the University of Virginia Law School where they had won the prestigious Moot Court Trial Award. Jay had gone on to private practice, with a specialty in Real Estate Law. His principal client, the I. M. Knot Hurt Company, had made him a millionaire.

Jay Cutler seemed to have it all, and sometimes Jack wondered if he himself had made the right choice "in the service of the people." He felt tired this morning, and though he kept fit with his daily run and workout schedule, Jack felt every one of his 41 years. To all appearances, Jay, looking both fit and relaxed, seemed full of energy.

"Come on, Jack," said Jay, as he repeatedly tapped the tennis ball in the air with his racket. "We need to get these guys early today. They're about ten years younger than us forty-something geezers. They think we're over the hill. Get that weary D.A. look off your face. We are better than these guys. They're young and I think they're in better shape. We've got to demoralize them early. Make 'em think they just can't beat us. You know, like you do in court. If it goes to a third set, they will beat us, cuz ole buddy, by then we will be out of gas. But they can't know that."

After a pause, Jay continued, "So, here's the plan. We come at 'em fast and hard, never let up, just like we did in Moot Court, eh, Jack?"

Jay slapped Jack on the back and they both laughed at his pep talk. They walked out to the tennis pavilion to introduce themselves to their younger opponents.

Jay was a shifty 'lefty' and Jack was known for his powerful forehand from the right. This immediately and temporarily confused their younger opponents. Jay and Jack won the first two games.

In the third game, Jack served a hard top spinner to the deuce court and Fred Unger and his partner, Bill Carter, stood frozen in place as Jay blasted the weak return shot into the open court. On the next point Bill Carter whipped a second serve down the line and Jack, with a lunge to his right, stopped the ball in mid-air and dropped it over the net — perhaps with a little luck — but it was a phenomenal shot. Jay Cutler chuckled and whispered to Jack loud enough for the others to hear, "You sure have that drop shot working today, Jack." Jack turned his back to the net as he started walking down to the deuce court. He was still smiling at the enjoyment of the moment.

With the score thirty-love on Jack's serve, Jack rocketed an ace down the T of the deuce service line. Forty-love and a second serve with a high top spin caught Fred Unger off guard yet again. His weak return was intercepted by Jay at the net and again slammed into the open court. Third game to Jay and Jack. Now it was 3-0 in the first set. More impressive, the "young guns" hadn't won a single point. They had a "Who are these guys?" look on their faces.

"A couple more games like this, and these guys are going to fold," Jay said to Jack, again loud enough for their opponents to hear. "Let's turn it on."

Fred Unger slammed his first serve to Jack. Jack caught up to the speeding ball as it spun wide to his right, and was just able to flick it down the line. He caught an embarrassed Bill Carter by going the other way. Love-fifteen. The visibly exasperated Fred Unger missed his first serve to Jay by "going for too much." Jay lined up the weaker second serve and slammed it at the feet of the on-rushing Fred Unger just as he was reaching mid-court. The ball literally spun off Fred's racket and dribbled off towards the tennis pavilion where the Saturday morning crowd was beginning to sense something special was happening on Court 5. Love-Thirty.

A double fault to Jack made it Love-forty. A lefty forehand return from Jay caught the youngsters off guard yet again. Another game to Jack and Jay — at Love — and still their opponents had yet to score a single point. This fact was not lost on them. Nor was a gathering crowd of spectators in the Pavilion about to let it go. "Hey, have you kids won a single point against these 'old men'? It looks like they've got a 'choke hold' on you." The crowd laughed good naturedly, because all tennis is supposed to be a good natured, good sportsmanship game. Still it was apparent to all that Jack and Jay had gotten into the heads of their opponents. They appeared to be dazed and confused, and a little annoyed. Jack overheard Fred Unger say to Bill Carter, "I can't believe this crap. We should be killin' these guys." But they did not appear to believe it themselves. The exuberant weekend crowd of spectators loved the early morning drama unfolding. It was as good as a Bloody Mary pick me up.

For Jack and Jay it was one of those magical tennis days when they could do no wrong. They were in the Zone. They moved in unspoken synchronicity, as one unit, from side to side, smothering the net and seeming to make difficult, even impossible, shots. Of course a faster, younger team like Fred Unger and Bill Carter couldn't be held scoreless forever, and as they began recovering some of their lost confidence, their youth and speed began to catch up with Jack and Jay. Almost imperceptibly, the momentum and the games seemed to move away from Jack and Jay.

Now it was 4-5 in Jack and Jay's favor with Fred Unger serving at thirty-forty to Jay. If Jack and Jay won this point, they won the set and could regain the momentum. If they lost, the game would go to deuce and with the on-rushing younger opponents beginning to turn it on, it was perhaps a turning point of the match. The four players on the court knew it and certainly the crowd of spectators sensed it.

Jay received a hard flat serve to his lefty forehand and chipped a "screamer" down the center between the "other guys." Both he and Jack, sensing their tactical advantage, rushed the net as Fred Unger scrambled in retreat to catch up to the ball. He was just able to reach it, and with the racket fully extended and with a perfect "flick of the racket," he lobbed it over the rushing Jack. Fred seemed to visibly relax as he watched his lob soar over Jack's head and deep into the baseline where it appeared Jack could simply not get to it in time. He watched with amusement from the baseline as he observed Jack race to catch up with what was obviously a top spin lob winner.

But then almost as in slow motion, Jack did reach the ball still going away from the net. He knew he would have to hit the ball really high if he was to have a chance to reverse its arc and send it back across the net. He did. A ball hit so high that all four players waited together to see where it would land. But the ball was momentarily impossibly hard to see. It had become lost in the morning sun. Exasperated, Fred Unger shielded his eyes with his left hand. Suddenly, he saw the ball drop out of the sunlight onto the baseline tape just next to him. The ball, having dropped literally out of the sky, its ongoing momentum carried it up again, high above the court in a lazy arc towards the giant hedges which framed the court. Fred raced back to the hedges desperately reaching up for the ball with his racket, much like a center fielder might reach up to rob a hitter of his homerun. To no avail. As Fred slammed into the hedges, he could only look up to see the ball land softly on the very top of the hedges, almost nesting.

The point was over. The game was over. And the first set belonged to Jack Forester and Jay Cutler. The players and the spectators were looking in amazement at the ball that was still nestled, for all to see, atop the hedges. There were the usual comments from the fans like "That was a hell of a shot, Jack." "I've never seen anything quite like it." There was a smattering of clapping, and then another voice from the crowd said, "Well, Fred, I think you boys are just going to get 'schooled' today. Might as well just lay back and take your medicine." The crowd laughed good naturedly, but Fred turned in the direction of the voice and said, "Screw you, Rogers." Now this outburst was understandable, given the way the last point had played out, but the crowd did not like it.

"Oh, it looks like Martha put a little too much starch in Fred's shorts last night," continued Joe Rogers. "Well, I figure they'll hang pretty loose once this match is over." The crowd laughed again, as everyone thought this last comment was pretty amusing, everyone except Fred and his partner.

As they prepared to begin the second set, Fred Unger whispered to his partner, "OK, let's quit screwing around and put these guy back where they belong – in their 'middle ages'." Unfortunately, Joe Rogers, who had moved his lawn chair to the very edge of the pavilion and practically onto the court overheard this last remark and loosely and loudly paraphrased it, "Hey Jack, Fred says you guys are too fat and too old to beat them a second set."

"Hey, that's not what I said, Rogers," yelled Fred from the court.

But it was already too late. Fred had taken the bait, and Jack capitalized on the moment. "Well, Fred, we've still got a little left in the tank for two old fat guys." He stared down at Fred in mock anger.

"Jack, I didn't say that." Fred was practically whining in his exasperation, but Jack, with a wink to Jay Cutler turned back in the direction of Fred and continued, "OK Fred, that's it. Let's just see what you can show us. Talk is cheap."

"Yeah," Joe Rogers agreed from the sidelines. "Let's see what you've got Fred."

"Shut up, Joe," said Fred, pointing his racket at his own personal heckler.

The whole pavilion was in an amused uproar. They knew now that Joe had "gotten Fred's goat," that is they sensed that Fred was losing his composure and was about to lose his temper.

"So," said Jack. "It's your serve, Fred. Any other gratuitous remarks, or can we continue? Jay and I would like to get going if you guys have caught your breath." There was more appreciative laughter from the pavilion, as Fred practically ran back to the service line.

Jack saw Fred wind up his serve with the words, "This one's for you Jack," and he proceeded to blast his first serve into the deuce court. Jack could not even get his racket on the ball, but it did not matter.

"Just wide, Fred," he said.

"Are you sure?" Fred was glaring across the net.

"It was wide." This from Bill Carter to his partner. "Come on, Fred. Second serve." Fred hit another blistering serve, harder than the first, but it was six inches too long.

"Double fault, Fred. Love-fifteen." It was Jay Cutler getting into the act.

"I know the score, Jay," said Fred as he proceeded to blast two more errant serves in the general direction of the ad court. Now it was Love-thirty to Jack and Jay.

Fred pushed his next serve into the deuce court and Jack drove it behind Bill Carter at the net and down the line, a clean winner. At Love-forty, Fred hit a sharply angled top spinner to Jay's backhand, or so he thought. He had momentarily forgotten that Jay was a "lefty," who consequently was able to get around the offering with a hard, forehand topspin which took the serve on the "rise" and drove it past the startled Bill Carter at net and just out of the reach of the hard charging Fred Unger. First game of the second set at "love" to Jack and Jay. Not even close. Fred had lost his serve, his biggest weapon, at love. It was more than a game to him now as Jack later observed.

Fred was embarrassed. His inner anger turned on his racket. He flung it at the hedges, which surrounded the courts. The handle was driven deep within the bush so that only the head was sticking out. Even the gathered crowd went silent at this outburst. A little ribbing, a little gamesmanship, and trading little sarcasms, good natured and not, was all considered part of the mental part of the game. Throwing your racket, as Fred had just done, was considered "over the line" juvenile and just not acceptable in the unwritten tennis etiquette rules. Everyone knew this at Farmington that morning, not the least of whom was Fred Unger.

Slowly he walked over, pulled his racket out of the hedges, and turned to the others on the Court. "Sorry, fellas. I guess it just slipped out of my hand."

At 1-0, he and Bill Carter crossed over to the other side. Everyone waited for another riposte from Joe Rogers, but there was none. It would have been too easy. Fred Unger was already a "broken man," and now he had even embarrassed his partner by his actions.

There were a few good rallies in the second set, but it appeared that Fred and Bill were just "going through the motions" as if they couldn't wait to get off the court and away from this match, this crowd, and the embarrassment of it all.

The second set was over in 25 minutes 6-2 for Jack and Jay. Fred and Bill walked slowly to the net, shook hands, and offered their congratulations. Then they practically raced off the court to avoid the good natured cat calls. Still, they must have overheard one in particular, "Old guys win — again!" It was Joe Rogers who now came out onto the court, turned to Jay Cutler, and said, "Well, how'd I do, Jay?"

Jay and Joe roared with laughter.

"Joe," Jay said, "that was the best bit of heckling I've seen."

"So do I trophy?" said Joe.

"Yes, absolutely. You've earned that six pack of Bud. Hell, I'll even drink it with you." Now Jay turned to Jack. "Yep, Joe was our secret weapon, Jack. I couldn't tell you about it, or you wouldn't have let me do it. Worked great, didn't it? The only thing worse for Fred Unger than losing so badly and then losing his temper would be to tell him that we set him up. He'd probably commit suicide in angst if we told him. So we better let sleeping dogs lie, eh, Jack? Fred will get over it. Might even make him a better man for the lesson. So will you join us in a celebratory beer?"

"No," said Jack with a level gaze at his erstwhile partner. "You two rogues, er, should I say 'partners in crime,' go enjoy the tainted victory." Then Jack chuckled as he turned to Jay again. "You know, Jay, I think we could have beaten them without Joe's antics. Now we'll never know. Joke's on us."

"Oh, come on, Jack. I was just looking for a little extra fun."

"And a little insurance," said Jack.

"Maybe. Hey, you on for next Saturday, same time? We're on a roll now. You and I."

"You and Joe are on a roll, not me. I'll pass on next week."

"Oh, c'mon Jack, don't be such a 'straight arrow.'"

"I guess we all have our true nature, Jay. Maybe that's why I work for the Commonwealth and you make all that money in real estate development." Jay stood speechless at this retort.

"See you later, Jay, Joe." Jack strode away to the comfort of his car, and the better company he now sought, Jack the dog.

People were such a disappointment after you got to know a good dog.

---

Jack found Jack the dog curled up in the driver's seat of his old convertible. The sun had shifted with the day. Its warm rays had pierced the previous shade and they were now providing Jack the dog an excellent sun bath. He was quite obviously asleep on the job.

"Oh, Jack," whispered his Master as he approached the car. As if levitated, Jack the dog bolted upright in his Master's seat, turning his head from side to side to show he had been guarding the car all along.

"Easy, boy," said Jack the man, opening the door and accepting a lick to the accompaniment of Tom Tom pounding of dog tail on the leather seat. "OK, move on over to your side. It may be Saturday, but we've got a lot of work to do before the weekend's over."

As if in total understanding (and why not), Jack the dog eased over to the passenger seat, his tail still wagging at the return of his Master. As they drove off down Tennis Lane, turned right onto Farmington Drive, and headed back to town, wind blowing in their hair, Jack reached over to scratch his dog behind the ears. He smiled as Jack the dog turned to show his teeth. It was the smile of joy. It was as if they shared that mutual thought, "It doesn't get any better than this."

And, of course, as all true dog lovers know - it really doesn't.

**Adapted from**

*Waiting on Nantucket*

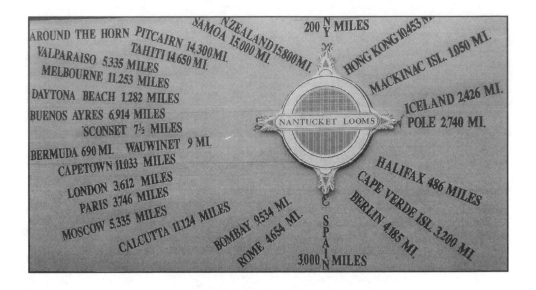

Fun Facts about Nantucket:

- Nantucket is a beautiful and magical island 30 miles out to sea off the coast of Massachusetts. It's about 14 miles long and four miles wide and has over 55 miles of ocean beach.
- There are currently 5,000 permanent residents and up to 55,000 summer people, but you can always find a beach where no one ever goes.
- Nantucket was discovered by Quakers fleeing the Massachusetts Puritans in 1659. There they also discovered about 500 Wampanoag Indians who had already been living on the island for several hundred years.
- Amazingly and beautifully, the Wampanoags welcomed the Quakers, helped them survive their first brutal winter, and taught them how to fish and hunt whales.
- At one time, the little island of Nantucket had the third largest whaling fleet in the world.

## FONDUE BLUES

Grenoble, France. It was March 1969. Joe Norton was treading water — not going to class — not seeing people… deep in Blue. He had cycled down to depression again.

Somehow, he had been talked into going to an early spring fondue party just outside Grenoble, at the student apartment of Christian Blaze, an English student. He had known him since early in the first semester. Although Christian had gone to an English boarding school, he was the product of an English father and an Italian mother, and seemed to have acquired, by turns a methodical, then suddenly explosive personality.

Amongst the twelve of us, the conversation jumped from upcoming vacations to academic plans for the following year, and, inevitably to the war in Vietnam. For the English, the Dutch, and even the Canadians in attendance, it was more of a philosophical discussion. But for the American students present, all draft eligible, it was a matter of life changing consequences.

"I won't go if they draft me," said Pepper McVey from Chicago. He was a tall, athletic 19-year-old who played goalie on the University of Grenoble international student hockey team. "I mean, I don't mind the challenge and I love my country, but this is a filthy colonialist war, thousands are dying for no good reason, and I find the carpet bombing of entire villages — men, women, and children — an abomination. No, sir. I'll go to Canada if they draft me."

There was a long silence as the rest of us dipped our cheese or steak bits into the boiling oil of the fondue pot. We wrapped it in bread and washed it all down with copious amounts of cheap, but good *vin du pays*.

"Norton, what would you do if you had it to do over?" asked Christian. "I mean you're a vet."

"Well, I didn't go to Vietnam," he said. "So I can't say for sure."

But Christian persisted. "You *were* in the service. Knowing what you know, would you be willing to fight over there?"

"I don't know," he said slowly. "Hindsight is a wonderful thing. Yes, I suppose I would go, but I would ask to be trained as a medical technician… something like that."

Still, Christian would not be denied. "You mean you would rather be a stretcher bearer than fight an unjust war?"

"That's not what I said."

"No, but I know that's what you mean," said Christian with absolute conviction, "and I find that admirable."

"Stretcher Bearer – Stretcher Bearer – STRETCHER BEARER."

Christian's words began to echo in Norton's head, and the room was spinning around him. He got up slowly from the group, who were still sitting cross-legged around the fondue pot. He knew he had drunk a fair amount of wine, and had taken a couple of tokes from the hashish pipe making the rounds. It was all supposed to make you infinitely mellow; yet suddenly he was feeling totally paranoid, depersonalized, as if he were standing outside a bubble looking in. He nodded to Christian, said he was going outside to get some air, and disappeared through the door.

---

Early spring in the foothills of the French Alps often brings subfreezing temperatures at night. He was cold and he zipped up his parka and pulled his collar up. Still, he had decided to walk the 10 kilometers back to his apartment in Grenoble rather than wait for a ride. He wanted to clear his head. He had to decide what he could do to lift this oppressive depression which he had kept at bay during Christmas in Abergavenny, Wales, but inevitably, it seemed, it settled in on his return to Grenoble. It had only deepened in the two months since then.

Was this then going to be his continuous roller coaster life? Was he gradually going insane? Was there any long-term solution? He knew he did not want to live the rest of his life like this. Was his illness behavioral or organic? Would he ever have a long-lasting relationship, or would they all be destroyed by the bitch goddess of depression?

One can cover a lot of ground in 10 kilometers of internal conversation and brisk walking. He reached his apartment, chilled to the bone, about two hours later. But he had reached one immediate conclusion: dammit, he was going to give his fragmented life one more chance to heal. He would reach out and try one more time for the stability he was looking for... but he had told himself that so many times before.

Nevertheless, as he opened the outer door that led up the stone steps to his third-floor room with a view of the kitchen across the alley, somehow he began to feel better. He just didn't know why.

*Travels with Sonya*

He did not know the nature of his illness in 1969, only that he was going through this incredible sense of self-loss for the second time in fewer than two years. Not knowing what caused it was frustrating. Not knowing how long it would last was frightening.

Such were his concerns as he hunkered down in his one room apartment. In this, his second semester at the University of Grenoble, his first semester neighbors had moved on to more attractive quarters. It was probably inertia that prevented him from doing the same. Meanwhile, his best friend, Gavin Farley, had taken a second-semester job teaching English in Bordeaux where he was hoping to play team rugby while learning about the local beers and wines. So, thought Norton, he was pretty much the last of the old guard.

There was one other holdover exception to the new co-tenants, most of whom socialized amongst themselves. That exception was an "Italian," Sonya Bice, who claimed to be from the small village of Piro, Italy, just north of Rome. She was a petite blond, fit and attractive, and, as it turned out, a great skier. He had often imagined taking her out, but she made it clear to him and his English-speaking friends that she preferred the French students. She was always hanging on the arm of one of them. Still, there was some question as to Sonya's real nationality, especially after their landlady brought her niece over to meet Sonya because, supposedly, they were both from the same Italian village. Sonya refused to come out of her room that entire weekend, claiming that she had a bad cold and did not want to give it to anyone. The cold miraculously disappeared just as soon as the niece had left to go home.

So, we were a little suspicious. Sometimes we would tell locker room jokes around Sonya, since she claimed to speak no English, to see if we could make her blush… but it was hard to tell through that ever-present tan. Now that the others were gone, Norton was pleased that Sonya was still around, even though they spoke only French in passing.

On this particular night, Norton had just walked back from the school cafeteria and was in his room sifting through a long, short story he kept revising. It was called "Thirty Days in the Brig," a little autobiographical memoir. He was convinced it could be a topical best seller, given the political situation, if he could just get it right. Yes.

He picked up this story from his bed, which also served as his horizontal filing cabinet during the day, and walked over to his desk. It was situated in front of a large window, facing over an alley. It looked directly into the communal kitchen beyond. He was just beginning to re-edit his story for the umpteenth time when the view across the alley into the kitchen caught his attention. There was Sonya, gesturing to one of the other boarders, Mustapha Caron, from Tunisia. Norton thought of him as "Must-Hava-Girl" Caron, as he was always asking him if I knew of any available "hotties." But as he watched Mustapha slowly following Sonya round and round the kitchen table, he noticed she was wagging her finger and smiling as if coyly telling him to back off. It all seemed harmless, until suddenly he saw Mustapha grab Sonya by the arm and pull her to him. She slapped him and ran out into the hallway with Mustapha close behind. Norton opened his door and she ran into his arms, and their momentum pushed them both back onto his bed.

Just at that moment, Mustapha appeared at the door. He was flushed and appeared a little embarrassed. "Oh, I did not know she was *your* hottie, Norton. I am so sorry."

Norton disentangled himself from Sonya, who remained on the bed. He told Mustapha he needed to take a long walk outside to cool off, and that if he ever saw him grabbing Sonya like that again, he would have the campus police charge him with assault.

"Oh, no, no, Norton," said Mustapha, slowly backing away. "It was just a mistake, never happen again. Sonya, Sonya, please forgive me …" All this as he backed down the hallway and disappeared down the stone steps to the street below.

"Thank you," said Sonya, in English as she sat up on his horizontal file bed. "That could have been bad."

"Hey. You're speaking English," Norton asked in a measured tone. "So, who are you and where are you really from?"

"My name is Sonya Bice, and I'm from Walnut Creek, California. It's a little town just outside of San Francisco."

"Well, I'm guessing you're not a spy. So what's with the Italian village girl disguise?"

"I just wanted to be French, speak only French, hang out with the French, and really *become* French for one year. That was my total immersion goal. I couldn't do that as an American from California. I had done an exchange program with an Italian family two years ago, so I thought I could pretend to be from a small Italian town no one had ever heard of."

Although Norton had always been somewhat suspicious about the true nature of this "Italian" girl, still he was amazed that she had been able to protect her cover for so long.

"So that's why you hid in your room with a cold when a real Italian girl from your alleged hometown came around?"

"Yes."

"And that's why you pretended not to understand the locker room jokes the boys and I tested you with?"

"Yes. By the way, they were pretty gross." They both laughed at the thought of it all. Then Sonya looked up at him and said softly, "You will protect my cover, won't you? It's very important to me."

"If that's what you want," he said.

Sonya reached over and covered his hand with hers. "It is," she said.

### Trip to Spain with Sonya

Norton never knew what brought on the Gluey Blue Demons of depression, how debilitating they would be or how long they would last — two months, six months, or longer. He did know he got more out of this protracted 'dead zone' than he thought while he was struggling through it and he did recognize the signs of coming out of it, whether it be increased spontaneity, wanting to be around people a little more, or starting to have more hopeful thoughts about the future.

And now he was beginning to experience some of that renewed hope just as he was deciding what he would do with his upcoming three-week semester break as scheduled by the University of Grenoble. Since he had no car, and no longer any close friends, he resolved to take the plunge on his own. He would hitchhike south to the warmth of the Spanish Mediterranean, stay a couple of weeks, and come home. It beat hanging around Grenoble, and he felt that he was ready for some newness.

Just at that moment, Sonya, who had acquired an old Peugeot earlier in the new year, appeared at his doorway to ask if he would like to drive north with her to Paris. She was going to meet with some friends from California who were attending the *Faculté Etrangère* the Sorbonne. He declined politely, saying he wanted to go south to Spain for the warmth of the sun and the beach, and just for the fact that he had never been there.

"Are you going with anyone?" she asked.

"No, but I don't mind," he said. "I've gotten used to traveling alone."

There was a pause. Then Sonya spoke again, "I guess it would be a lot warmer than in Paris at this time of year. I do love the sun. I bet you'll come back with a tan."

"I don't know about that," he said, "but it will be new and different for me, and I hear that the northern Mediterranean Sea is beautiful this time of year. It's still considered 'off-season' down there. There'll be cheap lodging and great seafood. Other than that, I guess I'll just walk the beach, smell the salt air, and …"

"And what?" Sonya wanted to know.

"Maybe get inspired on how to get on with the rest of my life."

Sonya started to walk away, then turned abruptly and said, "Norton, I don't really want to drive to Paris alone, and besides I've been there. Would you consider a traveling companion? We'll have my car and that will make it a lot easier. I think we could have a lot of fun. I mean it sounds like such an exotic getaway. Would you consider traveling with a friend and a car?"

He was surprised and a little intimidated by her offer, having not spent any concentrated time with anyone in about four months. But this would be brand new territory for both of them. Sonya had no expectations of him, so maybe it would all be part of his way back to himself again.

"Sure," he said slowly, shifting a bit on the side of his bed where he had been sitting. "How can I resist a traveling companion who provides her own car?"

---

His original hitchhiking destination had been Tarragona, a midsize city 80 miles south of Barcelona. He had read that it had beautiful beaches. But, now that they had a car, they decided they could go a little further south, still warmer and cheaper, to the small town of Salou. Here one could rent a small suite with a kitchen right on the beach for the unbelievable per diem of $2. This, according to his *Michelin Guide to Student Travel* was based on off-season rates, and upon availability. It also meant fewer tourists, which he considered a bonus. The small village was surrounded by orange groves, and contained numerous bistros with cheap Spanish wine and beer, and several little restaurants specializing in paella and other seafood delights… and all dirt cheap in the off-season.

Sonya was impressed with his description. It was as if he was convincing them both that this could be a great adventure together.

"You know, Norton," she said as she walked through the doorway and sat next to him on the bed, "you're really a nice guy. I'm glad I'm finally getting to know you."

"Thanks," he said.

"You're nice and relaxed and considerate, not as I thought you were before. I used to think you were obnoxious and loud…likable…but I much prefer you this way. Do you think you've changed since you came to France?"

"Yes."

"What do you think caused it?"

"Depression," he said in total deadpan fashion.

"Depression!" Sonya laughed heartily. "That's a hot one."

"Yes, it's the hottest," he said softly.

We were quiet for a while, and then Sonya turned to me.

"Are you really depressed, Norton?"

"A little," he said, "but I'm working my way out of it."

"Well, I don't want you to be depressed, but I really like you just the way you are." She leaned over and gave me a peck on the cheek.

Who knew that depression could work for you this way?

———

The way south to Barcelona and Salou on the Mediterranean seemed simple enough. The main highway was straight and broad almost the entire way, except for the mountain passes. According to his trusty Michelin guide there were many informal campgrounds along the way. They planned to stay in one their first night and arrive in Salou the afternoon of the next day.

They picked up provisions in a small French village just before their descent through the Pyrenees to the Spanish border on the other side. These included the usual fresh French bread enveloped by a torpedo shaped crust, butter, tomatoes and ham, all from a little farmers' market. It also included a bottle of water and some really good regional red wine. They even bought a little cream-filled gâteau for dessert.

They brought this bohemian feast to the next roadside campground, which was beyond the peak of the mountains and at a halfway point down the steep descent towards Barcelona. Here they found an excellent campsite from which they could see the Barcelona city lights flickering in the distance. Above them, were a clear sky and a million stars. As it happened, there was a full moon.

Sonya made the sandwiches while Norton cleared the ground for their sleeping bags. He gathered some kindling and made a small campfire. Then he poured the wine into small tin tumblers. They sat there in the warmth of the fire with their sandwiches, and drank to their good fortune.

It was delicious. Like old friends, they laughed and told stories of childhood, of the year in Grenoble, and lastly, their plans for the future. Hers were more concrete than his. "I'm going back to UC Berkeley to complete my degree in foreign languages. Then I will get my teacher's certificate. I plan to teach high school French or Italian, and I plan to travel for two months every summer during school vacation. That's my plan. How about you?"

"I don't know," he said slowly. "English and history have always been my interest. I'd like to get my degree, and then teach and write. Since I probably won't make any money from my writing for a while, and maybe never, I will teach in order to pay the rent. I like working with kids. I think I understand them better than most adults, so yeah, I would teach and write if it all works out."

"Hmmm…" said Sonya. "I like that plan too, but have you ever thought about going to a place like California to finish your degree? You like new starts, I think. And California would be a whole new and exciting way for you to complete your undergraduate studies. And think of the experience," she said, looking at him across the flames of the campfire. Sitting there cross-legged in the fresh cooling air of the Pyrenees with a glass of red wine in one hand, her ham and tomato sandwich in the other, there was his little spy-friend sitting just across from him through the embers of the fire, and all of Spain spreading out behind her. In this setting, she made it all seem possible. But then he caught himself. "No, I don't think so," he said, smiling over at Sonya. "Too expensive, and I probably wouldn't get accepted anyway. But I do like the idea of it." Without thinking, he walked over and sat down next to Sonya and put his arm around her. It seemed natural, two friends sharing their future around a campfire.

Suddenly Sonya stood up, and looked down at him. She was still smiling, but had become quite fierce as she continued her inquisition. "Norton, you've got a lot to offer and you've got some good basic ideas for your future, but now you need to make specific plans, you know, a plan of action."

"Well," he said, somewhat bemused. "I told you, my plan of action is to finish college and then teach and write."

"Yeah, but where? When? Listen, I just had this great idea. My Dad is an administrator and a professor. He's on the California Board of Regents, and he has been instrumental in streamlining the state college system. He knows people. He's a great guy and he could really help you if you want to go back to school in the San Francisco area. As for money, you can establish your residence in California in just 90 days. After that it's about 40 dollars per quarter for a resident in the state college system for all the courses you can take. Now you can't beat that anywhere else. So think about it." Then she stopped as suddenly as she had started, sat down next to him again, and said softly, "I mean it."

It was intriguing, but probably impractical. Still, he enjoyed considering it, theoretically. He had always been interested in considering anything… theoretically. It's like that one night conversation you have with a friend, that really doesn't change much, but still the shared intimacy draws you closer to each other. That's the way he chose to consider it. But Sonya, his little American-Italian spy, had read his thoughts. She put her hand on his knee, squeezed lightly, and broke into his thoughts. "No, I'm serious, Norton. I want you to think about it, and if you are at all interested, I can help make it happen."

With that, Sonya rose up yet again to her full height of 5'3," hands on hips, and flashed her dark eyes at him. She chuckled as she dropped her hands to her side. "All right, Norton, I'll let you off the hook tonight. It's getting dark so I'm going to get some sleep." She pulled off her sneakers, unzipped her sleeping bag and crawled inside.

"Mmmm, this has been a great day, Norton. Do you think we'll get to the sea and the beaches by tomorrow afternoon?"

"Yes," he said. "By tomorrow afternoon, we should be sitting on our own personal beach in Salou, drinking Sangria, basking in the sun with the cool, salt water lapping at our toes."

"Mmmm…" and she was asleep.

---

Usually, he was an early riser, but this time it was Sonya who awakened him at 4 a.m. "Norton, I'm freezing, and I can't get back to sleep." Sure enough, a clear night sky in the foothills of the Pyrenees can turn a cool spring evening into winter-like conditions in those hours before morning. The temperature had dropped some 30 degrees since sunset. It was near freezing.

"Well," he said, looking over from his sleeping bag to Sonya, who was visibly shivering in hers. "There are only two things we can do to warm up."

"What are they?"

"Well, I could crawl in your sleeping bag with you. Our mutual body heat will warm us up pretty fast. It's a well-known camper's fact."

"O.K., nix to that Don Juan," Sonya interjected. "What's suggestion #2?"

"Hmmm. Now it's a little less inspiring, but probably as effective, I suppose."

"Well, hurry up. What is it ?" said Sonya.

He realized then that the cold had effectively erased Sonya's previous sense of humor.

"O.K.," he said. "All we have to do is pack everything back in the car, get going, turn the heater on, and within 10 minutes that blast furnace of a heater will have us warm as toast."

"Well, why didn't you say so?" said Sonya, jumping out of her sleeping bag and standing over him. She reached down to give him a playful shove, but he was quicker than she thought. He reached up and pulled her down playfully, but like a nimble wrestler she used the momentum to roll out of his grasp and back on her feet again. She winked.

"Now. Let's get going, Norton."

They broke camp quickly, stowed their gear in the '59 Peugeot, and were on their way south in 15 minutes. In a few minutes, the Peugeot's great old heater was putting out wonderful heat from the engine, and they were content to drive into the daylight. There was a comfortable silence, except for the occasional conversational fragment. "Are you a Don Juan, Norton?"

"I don't think of myself that way, Sonya. Do you think of yourself as the American-Italian from Piro by way of California?"

"To everyone but you, Norton." Then she wagged her finger at him. "You'd better honor my confidence."

"Of course. If that's what you want." He said, "You can think of me as your confidence handyman."

She leaned over and gave him a friendly punch in the shoulder in a way that made them both laugh. He also noted that she had a pretty sharp right jab.

Eight hours later, having crossed the Spanish border, driven through the major seaport of Barcelona, then through Tarragona and numerous other smaller towns, suddenly the road narrowed. Almost seamlessly, they found themselves in the small fishing village of Salou, which looked straight out onto a vast beach spreading into the Mediterranean Sea. It was around 4 p.m., and the sun was still bright, as it warmed them from a clear, azure blue sky.

"I think we've just found Paradise," he said.

"Well, let's find our $2 luxury condominium before we get too excited," said Sonya, ever the practical one.

---

"Parlez vous francais? Italiano? Espanol?" asked Sonya of the diminutive caretaker, gardener, and landlord of their eight-unit condominium complex.

"Yes, but I speak the English very fine, too." Sanchez took great pride in his broken English. He refused to speak to them in any other language. "This a bootiful condolinium," said Sanchez doing a virtual pirouette in the narrow hallway. "Behind us a full kitchen with all the utensils and down the hallway is towlet with shower, and of course straight ahead, we have the din din table and beyond that your queen size marital baid, very comfy, very amrous."

Sanchez smiled broadly, kissed his own hand and winked. "How long have you kiddos been married?"

"Just under a year," Norton said quickly. He put his arm around Sonya's shoulders and whispered in her ear, "We can't rent this place unless they think we're married. That's according to the rental agreement I just signed. I get the sense they're Catholic and very strict about that kind of thing around here."

"Ah, and the courtiyard," said Sanchez, continuing without missing a beat. "I will bring you beautiful fruit from it every day." He pointed out the window beyond us as he gradually made his retreat. "Thank you for your deposit. I hope you enjoy it here like a second honeymoon." Sanchez smiled brightly, and disappeared down the steps.

"I think he knows we're not married," Norton said to Sonya after Sanchez had left. "He's not much older than we are, and I think he can read the signs. Still, the rental agreement is explicit and he must report to the owner, so we all have to play the charade."

"That's fine by me," said Sonya. "I'm happy to play the part as your wife, and I can shed my Italian disguise for a while, *darling*."

"Excellent," he said.

"One caveat," said Sonya.

"Yes?"

"That queen-size bed over there is for Mrs. Norton only. Mr. Norton will have to sleep on the floor."

"Oh, Mrs. Norton. That's so cold."

"You'll be fine in your sleeping bag. Just fine."

Indeed.

———

By now it was too late to go to the beach. Sonya walked to a small grocery market they'd seen down the block while Norton did the unloading. Upon her return, she cooked a hearty spaghetti carbonara in their tiny new kitchen, and they dined al fresco on the small balcony overlooking the courtyard. There they observed ubiquitous Sanchez tending flowers and fruit trees, and occasionally waving up at them. As the sun set and the light started to fade, he heard Sanchez call up to them. "I bring you fresh fruit in the morning."

It was getting chilly, so they moved back inside, and Norton closed the sliding glass door behind them. They found themselves sitting at the small dining table, drinking the hot espresso that he had made in the kitchen. They looked back over the proverbial marriage bed through the glass door to the courtyard, and the setting sun on the horizon. They had no formal music, but they could hear the sounds of the birds in the courtyard speaking to each other and saying good night to the sky.

"This is nice," he said.

"It's fantastic," said Sonya. "O.K., Mr. Norton. I'm going to get ready for bed, my bed that is. You'd better pull out your sleeping bag, *darling*."

Maybe this is the best situation of all, he thought; two friends sharing a great traveling experience. And I'm starting to feel good again, for the first time in a long time. He thought *"L'amour"* could only complicate a beautiful friendship. As the French say, *"Soyez content."*

But they could not leave it at that. It was a relationship that had taken on a life of its own. Sooner or later, it was going to pull them to the next level.

On that very next morning, he heard a knock on the door. He scrambled out of his sleeping bag to answer it. It was Sanchez, beaming. He handed him a large wooden basket with mangos and oranges, peaches and bananas. "Good morning to you two love birdies. I bring you fruit, no charge. There is no other peoples here yet. Who else I gonna give it to? I think it will be a beautiful day for you peoples." He backed up and smiled, and then he was gone.

"Get over here, Mr. Norton." It was Sonya, sitting up like an imperial queen on her bed.

"Mmmm...let me try out one of those peaches."

He walked over to the bed and Sonya flung open the covers. "It's cold. Come on in and we'll have a little breakfast in bed... but no funny business."

"No promises," he said, slipping under the sheets and pulling them up.

Sonya took one bite from her peach and paused. "This is really good, fresh, succulent, and juicy. Mmmm."

Then she took the bowl that he had placed between them, and lowered it to the floor beside her. She sighed and then turned to him. "I think you better come over here, Mr. Norton, and make me warm."

"If that's what you want, Mrs. Norton."

Sonya reached over and pulled him to her. "I thought about it all night, ... and that's what I want."

———————————————

For them, sex meant the intimacy of mutual passion and all the joys of the moment. Though it was not the center of their relationship, it became the symbol of their mutual commitment. They laughed and kissed in public.

They held hands everywhere they went. After all, they were supposed to be this newly married couple, enjoying all the aspects of young love. It was all so easy in the anonymity of Salou. But he knew it was going to get complicated as soon as they got back to Grenoble. Better enjoy the moment.

With Sanchez's help, they found the perfect little beach where they could tuck themselves in amongst the dunes to hide from the blowing sand and still feel the rays of the sun on their skin. On occasion, they would run out and fling themselves into the frigid surf, towel off briskly, and walk the beach, a beach that belonged only to them and the seashells and the seagulls gliding above.

But in a few days, the springtime vacationers who had already begun to trickle in, would soon be arriving in droves. Their exquisite beach would become crowded, and their private condo compound would be brimming over with not so young married couples and children everywhere. Of course, Sanchez would be happy and fulfilled. The more requests and demands that he could satisfy, the better he liked it. But, for them it was time to leave, to head back to Grenoble, and to plan their future.

Along the way north, Sonya insisted on going to a bullfighting event in the town of Tarragona. She had seen the posters for a bullfight that was to be held there on this day, and she was determined to taste this part of Spanish culture, even as he was not. They pulled off the highway and followed the signs, visible everywhere, to the arena.

When they arrived, he bought some lower-level seats where they could see it all. They watched as gaudily dressed clowns, much to the delight of the crowd, taunted the bull. They saw the bull being softened up by the sharp lances of the mounted picadors, much to the oohs and aahs of the crowd. And they saw the matador strutting out with his red cape, taunting him again and again with every sweep of his cape until the bull charged. They watched the matador feint one way and the next, fooling the bull and garnering various *olés* from the crowd. Then they saw the picadors attack the bull again. This time they rode along at his side, as they lanced him again and again.

Finally, the bull stumbled to his haunches. Now with a grand smile of triumph, the matador waved his bloody cape as he looked to the crowd. Had the bull done well? Should he spare him? The crowd yelled no and they gave the thumbs down signal.

Tipping his hat in deference to the crowd, the matador advanced on the helpless bull, raised his long sharp executioner's sword, and neatly shoved the instrument just behind the shoulder blade and straight down to pierce the heart of the bull. It was a clean kill. The bull lurched over to his side and was still. He was dead. Wild applause followed from the bloodthirsty crowd. Bravos all around, except for one toothless old lady who leaned over to him and said in broken English, "I don't think your girlfriend feel too good. Maybe she don't like the blood."

Sonya's face was a kind of greenish pale. She looked like she might throw up. "Let's get out of here," she said. "Quick."

"So much for the Spanish and the beauty of bullfighting," Norton said.

"I had to experience it," said Sonya, as they got back in the car. "But, I never want to see another."

He reached over and squeezed her hand as they drove off. "Good. That's something else we can agree on."

She squeezed back. And then, as only Sonya could do, and just as he was growing comfortable with their shared thoughts and understanding, she surprised him again with a revelation from her secret world.

"Norton," she said, rolling down the window and breathing in the cold fresh air. "I've been in touch with my Dad and I told him all about you."

"When did you find time to do that?" he asked.

Sonya smiled and told him she had made the call on the way to the corner market a few nights before.

"Why didn't you tell me about the call then?" he asked.

"I wanted to wait for the right time."

"Like after a bullfight?" he asked.

"No, silly. Like when we're in the car going back to Grenoble and we have plenty of time to talk. Like now silly boy. And it's all good news."

Yeah. The secret side of Sonya was beginning to concern Norton. Still, he focused on the good news she brought from her conversation with her Dad. It seemed her father would be happy to shepherd this special friend of Sonya's into the California college system. All Norton needed to do was to forward his transcripts, together with a letter detailing what he had been doing since he left school, and why he wished to return. Mr. Bice would even help him polish the letter if Norton would send him a rough draft. It could all be done, and Sonya's parents would even let him stay in their pool house during summer school for the 90-day residence requirement. Unbelievable, he thought.

Sonya continued. "The plan is for me to return to my apartment in Berkeley, and register for the fall semester there. So, what do you think of that plan of action, Norton?"

"Well, I'm a little stunned by it all, and a little surprised that you're just now telling me about it. I was still thinking in the theoretical, but I've got to admit it sounds great."

"Well, I think it's time you got out of the theoretical and into the practical, don't you?"

"Yes," he said. "Let's do it." He felt a little bit like the straw man from the Wizard of Oz who has just had his stuffing replaced. It felt good, a little scary, but good, this getting back into life. "I think I'm ready for your practical world."

"Good. I thought it would make you happy. It makes me happy too. There's only one thing," she continued.

"Uh, oh, here we go again."

"At the beginning of this semester, I put in a bunch of job applications for summer jobs around Europe, just to see what was out there before returning home. Well, just before we left for our trip to Spain, I got an offer from Club Mediterranean to teach water skiing on the Greek Island of Corfu. Apparently, they liked my language abilities as well as the fact that I am a certified Red Cross instructor and have water-skied since I was six years old. I agreed to work there from the six-week period from June through the middle of July."

"Why didn't you tell me *that* before?"

"Because we were only friends then. Now all that's changed, and I want to share everything with you."

*On a need to know basis*, he thought to himself. The secretive side of Sonya kept reemerging. Still, she was so persuasive. "Oh, look Norton. Don't worry. We're going to share everything after this summer. I know it. By the time you're well settled into summer school at Cal State Hayward, I'll be finishing with my assignment in Corfu. I'll be coming home, and we can begin talking about our future together."

Hmmm. *What future*, he thought as they drove back toward Grenoble. This was only part of Sonya's unilateral scenario, and much of it, he sensed, she had yet to share with him. For example, they hadn't even discussed moving in together. And frankly, he didn't know if he was ready for that or the further commitment that might imply. Yet, Sonya simply assumed things. And she assumed that everything would evolve accordingly.

"Norton, Corfu will be a good break for us. I'll miss you terribly, and I'll write you every day. But it will all make getting back together so much sweeter, because I…um…think I…um…love you."

His hands went clammy on the steering wheel and he felt his heart sink. Sonya had worked out their present and his immediate future, pretty much without his participation. He really cared for her and the friendship they had built. He loved the fun and good times, and he wanted the best for her and her future. He even loved her quirky secretiveness, although it bothered him at the same time.

What he did not know was whether he was truly in love with her, or she with him.

It was going to be an interesting summer.

### Kaleidoscope Notes from the Summer of '69

Most of the plan worked out just as Sonya had predicted it would … most of it. Norton went back to the States and worked his way out to Walnut Creek, California, to stay with Sonya's parents, the Bices. Of course, Sonya was in Corfu and would arrive home in a few weeks.

Meanwhile, and as part of his conditional acceptance at Cal State Hayward, he was to complete two history courses in summer school, both with a required grade of B or better. For once, he really studied and he received an A average in both courses. The Bices were great people, very supportive, and invested in his success as someone important to their daughter… how important? None of them knew, including Sonya. Norton maintained the pool in exchange for the rent of the pool house.

As one might have guessed with Sonya, there soon appeared a new issue to resolve. Although she had said she would write Norton every day upon reaching Corfu, he heard from her only twice during her time there. The first was a four-line postcard in which she said the island had yet to be electrified, so there was no light in which to write at night (what about lanterns?), and there were no breaks to do so during the day. This card was her only opportunity. She ended it by saying, "Talk to you in a couple of weeks. Love ya — Sonya." The second card, even briefer, said she had been extended by three weeks, but couldn't wait to see him.

Yeah, right. The final blow came just two days after receiving the second card when he was at the local 7-Eleven. He was standing in the checkout line when he happened to notice a tabloid headline, *Greek Royalty Parties Big on the Playground Island of Corfu.* He nearly dropped his grape Slurpee as he reached for the article and read the text, which included the interesting tidbit that the Island of Corfu had been electrified, on behalf of the Greek Royals, some 15 years before.

He had to face facts. This was beyond subterfuge. Sonya had said there was no light to write at night, and of course there was. But why? Because she was lazy? No. Because she was having too much fun and was not that motivated? Maybe, or because she had met somebody else?

Whatever her motivation, she had deceived him; in fact, she had absolutely lied to him. This left him distrustful and with very cold feet. Maybe she was just living in the moment and couldn't help herself, but still she had betrayed his confidence. He couldn't accept that. With a regretful good-bye to the Bices, he moved out of their pool house and into an apartment in Hayward with some school friends.

Many years later, he learned that Sonya had come back at the end of the summer of '69 and returned to Berkeley where she got a degree in languages. She then earned a graduate degree from the Sorbonne. She married one of her French professors. Norton heard she had three French-American children and she brought them to California each summer. He had not heard from Sonya since the beginning of the summer of '69 until

February 1978, when she wrote him a full history of her life. She had been amicably divorced from Jean Paul since 1974 and had happily returned from France to San Francisco with her children. He did not know how she got his address, probably from his parents.

She wrote that she would love to see him as she was coming back to the East Coast and would be in New York City to visit a friend. "It's been too long. Write me and we will arrange a rendezvous."

One thing Norton knew for sure. Even though he had fond memories of Sonya, he could not handle her in his life right now... if ever. And that's when he realized he really did need to get away from his New York advertising job, more than ever; he was beginning to feel the return of the Gluey Blue Demons of depression.

Yes, he needed to break away. Not to Sonya but to a place like the Island of Nantucket, a little elbow-shaped island 30 miles out to sea, known to be friendly to lost souls and writers alike.

It was a place where he could go and write and be left alone, except for his dog.

And so he did.

## DORA DAYS
*200 Cliff Road, Nantucket, early summer 1978*

On that morning I followed my usual habit of writing from three until dawn.

About 5:30, just as the sun was coming up, I gathered my cocker/dachshund partner for an early morning beach walk. After Mystery had attacked the waves sufficiently to drive them away before they could come back at her, we returned home for breakfast.

After breakfast we drove down to Nantucket Centre and parked on Main Street next to the Club Car restaurant. There was plenty of shade and parking at 8 a.m., and I left the windows down, telling Mystery to stay in the car until I returned. Then I walked straight up Main Street to the Hub, purchased my Boston Globe and New York Times, and repaired to my favorite bench facing inward for better people observation. I read the news and checked up on the Red Sox. Today's coverage of yesterday's Red Sox game included a satisfying 4-0 shutout of the Baltimore Orioles. All this gave me and most of my fellow sports readers some added pleasure to start the day.

I gave the news and sports a full perusal. Good. Red Sox win again. Then, I walked two blocks over to the Athenium Library to do some research on the history of Nantucket. After two hours or so, I returned to my car and Mystery. As usual, she was waiting impatiently in the front seat.

I had called Mel, the owner of The Whale Restaurant, before I came to town to see if I could change my waiter shift from dinner to lunch for a while, something to do with my writing, I said.

"No problem," said Mel. "I'm short on day people."

"So, I'm in?" I said.

"As of right now, Norton, you are the king of the day shift. You start tomorrow. See you at 11:00 for prep."

"That sounds good," I said.

I walked over to The Tavern Restaurant on Straight Wharf. I knew it would be closed this early in the morning so I had put a note in an envelope addressed to Dora when she arrived for her luncheon shift in a couple of hours. It read, "*Dora, I too have switched to the luncheon shift at The Whale in part so that I can have dinner with you tonight and maybe again tomorrow night. Cocktails begin at 5:30. Dinner and starlight guaranteed barring fog. No RSVP necessary. Mystery and I will wait in anticipation — Norton.*"

I pinned the envelope to the door and headed home.

Since I was off tonight and didn't start my lunch shift until tomorrow, I had plenty of time to do a little outdoor work this afternoon, like replacing a few shingles which had blown off the roof in last night's wind. But first, I would give Mystery a nice little walk to Maxey's Pond just down a small hill from the cottage.

After a generous walk with Mystery, my 4-year-old cocker mongrel partner, I sat down at my little pine desk and turned on my adjustable student lamp and contemplated the next sentence. Still, I couldn't help but wonder if Dora had actually gotten my note and, if so, would she accept my open dinner invitation. Would she show up tonight?

I realized now I should have given her some space before assaulting her like a puppy dog wagging his tail frantically.

"Mystery," I said to my constant companion curled up in her usual position just in front of my writing table, "I might have really screwed this up. What do you think?"

Mystery looked up at me earnestly, trying to understand my words, and thumped her tail twice. "Ah, so you're saying it's gonna be okay. So, you think Dora will show up tonight?"

This time Mystery thumped her tail three times, stood up and stretched.

"Okay, Mystery, are you saying she will come or are you saying it's time for a walk?"

She trotted over to the outside door and looked back at me meaningfully. Then she barked, several times.

"Oh, I know what that means," I said, standing up. "You don't know if Dora is coming or not but you certainly *do* want a walk." I walked over and opened the door and stepped out with Mystery into the warmth of a bright sun, no fog, no clouds and about 70 degrees. The only thing missing was Dora.

I looked at my watch. Uh, oh, Dora would be coming about 5:30 if she were to arrive at the same time as yesterday … and if she came at all. It was 5:00. I'd better get going. A three-minute shower and an extended search for clean matching socks (Remember, I'm a bachelor.) I searched for jeans that were clean and not too wrinkled as it promised to be a cool night. Found. Now, where was that navy-blue Lacoste knit shirt I had washed this morning in hopes of wearing it for this very same occasion? Oh, there it was on a hanger draped over a floor lamp. It was still damp − but what the hell − dry enough for my body heat to make it go from damp to dry (Does that sound like a bachelor?)

And there was my white cotton sweater which I had earlier spot cleaned with a little soap and water and frantic rubbing of the fabric back and forth over those stubborn food stains. Amazingly, it had worked.

All dressed and my sweater hanging at the ready, I set up my big surprise. I was going to ask Dora to go back into town for a dinner date at Cap'n Tobey's Chowder House, home of the Island's finest clam chowder since 1956, and featuring lobster and other wonderful fresh fish. I had reserved a table on the second floor where there was a romantic water view of the Nantucket harbor.

Now it was past 5:30. Mystery was at the ready, lurking at the door, or was she just looking for another walk? It was sometimes impossible to know what Mystery did know, but she did know something.

I wandered around the house, tidying up, and readying a bottle of Chianti and a plate of my famous Ritz crackers with slabs of cheese. There would be our usual cocktail hour to be followed by dinner in town. I walked out on the porch, Mystery at my side. I could still see clear blue sky and the sun setting above Madaket to the West … a glorious romantic evening was in the offing.

Six o'clock and still no Dora. I opened the screen door and sat on the top step. Mystery settled right beside me. I gave her a little pat. She really was my best friend.

By 6:15 I knew Dora would not be coming. She was, like me, prompt by nature so if she wasn't here by now, I figured she would not be coming.

"Come on, Mystery. Let's go inside and have some crackers and cheese. I'll pour some wine for me and (pointing to her water bowl) I see you already have your beverage of choice."

I stood up and turned to go inside when my eye caught the silhouette of a figure on a bicycle just turning into my driveway. It was Dora. I watched as she hopped off her bike and walked it up the driveway to avoid having her beautiful derriére being assaulted by rough rock and sand as it had me a little earlier.

She smiled brilliantly, first at Mystery then at me. She was beautiful.

"Sorry I'm late, Norton. My roommate wasn't able to drive me so I had to ride my bike. It was a lovely ride but I didn't want to be late. Will you forgive me?"

Would I? I said to myself. "You bet I would."

Mystery jumped off the steps, tail wagging furiously, as she scampered down the steps to greet Dora … and Mystery doesn't do that for everyone.

Dora was delighted with my plan. "I love Cap'n Tobey's," she said. "Wonderful food and nicely informal with the view of the harbor, if you're lucky."

"I think we're going to be lucky," I said smiling.

First, a glass of wine and crackers all around, and then goodbye to a slightly sulky Mystery and off we went to town in the old station wagon.

We parked in Nantucket Town on Centre Street, a little off the main drag. Early summer was already approaching and parking was getting to be a problem. We didn't mind walking. Many of the shops were open and virtually all of the restaurants. There was even a new pizza parlor just off Main Street which was attracting customers, not only for their New York style pizza, but also for a giant bug zapping machine which hung down from just above the entry door. It provided an electrical discharge every time it dispatched a mosquito into the next world — great visual and auditory entertainment while eating a slice or two.

### Cap'n Tobey's and the White Elephant

We turned left on Upper Main Street just below the Pacific Bank. Here, for the "Evening Trade," there were art galleries, famous restaurants like the Opera House and the Club Car. We walked south on Lower Main Street to Cap'n Tobey's. Here we were seated at a second-floor corner table with a window looking out on the harbor lights, shimmering across the water and past various boating silhouettes.

Dora smiled and said, "This is wonderful." And it was.

With a cup of clam chowder for starters, I had oysters on the half shell and a main course of halibut. For Dora, it was Clam's Casino, lobster salad with fresh greens, and Atlantic Sea scallops. Well, that's a lotta fish, but it was magnificent.

Two glasses of champagne later for Dora, and a couple of dry gin martinis for me, mellowed out a lovely evening. For dessert, we shared a large piece of key lime pie.

It was about 9:30. Somewhere along the way Dora's hand had slipped into mine.

"Hey, let's go to the White Elephant," I said. "It's too early to say good night. They have a great bar and an even better piano player."

"Well, I don't know," said Dora smoothly, "but I do like to dance. Do you think we could share a dance over there?"

"Yes, I think we can do anything we want."

"Mmm," said Dora.

Everything in Nantucket Center is within walking distance, and we walked hand in hand to the White Elephant. The nightly fog had set in. We sauntered along, feeling deliciously invisible to all but ourselves. Almost too soon we arrived. We entered the piano bar where there was a jazz man playing licks on his piano and happy people drinking and milling around. I went to the bar and ordered two glasses of champagne. We found a corner and slow danced to a haunting piano improvisation of an old Billie Holiday song. And then the piano man kicked it off with some Fats Waller... and little jitter bugging from us.

Afterwards, we took our glasses out into the cool of the night. I turned to Dora and smiled. "I should probably get you home," to which she replied, "I'm in no hurry. Let's have a nightcap at your place."

We drove home to a welcoming canine.

Dora and Mystery settled on the porch, and I went in to get a couple of glasses and a white sauterne which I thought would provide a nice finish to all that fish we had eaten earlier. I returned to find Dora on her rickety wicker chair with Mystery parked right next to her. Dora smiled and looked over at me and said, "Norton, I'm feeling so good, but I'm also feeling a little sleepy. I wondered, can I stay the night?"

"Of course, you can."

Dora got up from her chair, leaned down and kissed me. "I love being with you, Norton." She smiled and disappeared into the house. Mystery trotted in with her, maybe in hopes of getting a treat. I waited for them to return. I was excited but a little apprehensive. I didn't want anything to ruin the moment ... or the future.

After waiting about five minutes, I walked into the house to look for Dora. I found her in the bedroom. She had tucked herself into my bed and was wearing one of my old flannel shirts. She was asleep. Mystery was curled up on a throw rug right next to her. I pulled up the comforter at the end of the bed and gently covered her. Momentarily she looked up, smiled and closed her eyes again. She looked comfortable, very comfortable ... and I sure liked having her around.

I slept on the couch in the living room. Let Dora have her peace and her sweet dreams. I noticed Mystery did not leave her side to join me in the living room. Maybe she was on sentry duty against all possible intruders, even me.

I went to the closet and pulled out an old Army blanket. It smelled like Dad and World War II and that's probably where it came from. Still, it was heavy and warm. I draped the whole thing around me. I was just thinking how nice it felt to have Dora in the house with Mystery and me … and I must have dropped off.

*Bicycle Ride for Three*

As usual, I got up around 3 a.m. to begin my writing time. I made coffee and filled Mystery's water bowl. Then I sat down at my desk and began to write. I had been thinking about a story of a man sitting at a café in the early morning when he sees a beautiful girl across the street. She is staring into a large rectangular clear glass window, watching a group of half-dressed mannequins. Is she the window dresser, he wonders, or is she just gazing at her own reflection? And then he sees that she is walking across the street towards him. Had she seen his reflection staring at her in that same window? When she arrives, do they have a casual conversation or something more meaningful … perhaps mysterious? What are some of the other twists and turns of the story? Is there a surprise ending? Is there tragedy involved? Or is there just resolution of the problems presented along the way?

I thought, instead of plotting it out and making an outline as I often did, I would just go ahead and write the story as it came to me … just to see what my imagination would bring. The editing and rewriting could come later. Almost like automatic writing, I would let my pen describe the images as they came to me. Sometimes it is like magic. I couldn't get the words down fast enough as the images flowed from my imagination. I was in a kind of writing zone. My words were like painting on paper the very visuals I was seeing. I did not know when I would lose that magic so I just kept at it. Of course, I didn't know how it would all develop or how it would end until I actually got there. What later became an eight-page short story emerged and concluded itself in a scant 2 ½ hours of feverish writing. Good or bad, it was quite an effort.

I reread the piece with some degree of satisfaction when the bedroom door opened and there stood Dora still dressed in my old flannel shirt. Mystery was at her feet looking at me a bit sheepishly as if to say, 'Well, I had to protect her. You understand, don't you?'

I smiled at both of them.

"Well," said Dora, as she pushed a bit of uncombed hair away from her eyes, "Mystery and I slept wonderfully, but I didn't mean to keep you from your bed."

"I was very happy to give it up, Dora, just to have you with me and Mystery. Now, may I offer you some of my best Nescafe instant coffee?"

"Yes," she said, "I would love some with cream."

"Milk be okay?"

"That would be divine."

I gave her a cup of hot instant coffee with milk and said, "You're easy to please".

"When I'm happy, I'm very easy to please," said Dora. She lifted up the yellow pad on my desk. "What have you been working on?"

I told her about *Girl in the Window*.

"I don't know if it is any good but it was fun to write."

"Well that's a good sign," said Dora. "May I read it?"

"Sure. Right now?"

"Yes."

I handed her the manuscript, "Okay, I'll just take Mystery for a quick walk down to the water. She likes company on her morning constitutionals. Anyway, that will give you time to read the story. Come on, Mystery, let's go on down to Maxey's Pond and check on the fish." With that we disappeared out the kitchen door.

Mystery and I sauntered down to the pond. It was about a twenty-minute round trip from the cottage. All the while, I was like a little kid wondering what the teacher would think of his homework. I realized in that moment how much I had fallen for Dora. It was important that she like my writing because it was a big part of me.

We reached the shoreline of the pond. Mystery tested the water temperature, daintily with a front paw which she quickly pulled back, and then disappeared behind one of the gnarly moor bushes which guarded the shoreline. Having completed the necessaries, she returned to me with a hop in her step.

"Come on, Mystery," I said. "Let's go home and see what Dora thought of our short story."

We reentered the cottage by way of the side porch screen door only to find Dora reinstalled on her chaise lounge. The early morning sunlight was filtering through the screen. She had pulled my Army blanket over her legs to shield them from the early morning chill. She was just putting down my manuscript.

"Well," I said cheerily, "Ça va?"

"I've read it twice," said Dora, "and to be honest, I'm a little bit jealous."

This was not what I had expected. She laughed as she saw my surprise. "Let me explain, Norton. I think it is really an intriguing story and with some self-editing you will make it really good."

"Excellent," I said, smiling broadly. "But what about the *jealous* part?"

Dora looked me straight in the eye and said, "That's because I think you really love the girl you have created. And, hypothetically, I was hoping you might come to like me as much as you like her."

"Is that a hypothetical?" I asked.

"Yes, strictly hypothetical."

## CHICKEN BOX BROTHERHOOD

I had been assigned the 3-11 p.m. shift at the Finast Supermarket in Nantucket's mid-island area. I was working in the deli as a sort of "time out" from waiting on tables which had left me a little burned out.

When my current shift was finally over, I reflected on the quantity of salami and pastrami and ham and prosciutto I had sampled between filling orders for customers. I was losing my taste for it, even if it did represent a free dinner.

I waved good-bye to my colleagues and headed across the street to the parking lot behind the Chicken Box Bar and Restaurant. This is where I had parked my old Chevrolet station wagon under a shade tree, eight hours earlier. This is also where I had left Mystery with plenty of ventilation, except for one brief walk about four hours earlier when I took my work break.

The Chicken Box parking lot was usually packed with pickup trucks and large old American cars, bikes, motorcycles, and a couple of vintage sports cars. (The Chicken Box was known as a local's bar and these were their vehicles parked outside.) Suddenly I saw Mystery, obviously outside of my car. She was sniffing at something in the high grass next to it. She had obviously jumped out of the blown out rear window and probably had been running around for some time. She could have been hit or run over by other vehicles in the parking lot, and this upset me. Usually, I might have been somewhat amused, but it had been a long shift. I was tired and I was thirsty.

"Get back in the car," I said sternly. She looked up at me and wagged her tail, pretending she had done nothing wrong. I raised the ante. "Damnit, Mystery. You heard me. In the car."

"Are you talking to me?" It was a voice from out of the dark just behind me. "I'm Mr. Reed, are you talking to me?"

I looked around, startled. In the meantime, Mystery raced over to the old Chevy, took a flying start from the sandy ground below and jumped right through the rear-view window frame and into the back seat. Meanwhile, a scraggly bearded guy, all arms and legs and wearing a dirty Captain's hat, strode out from the shadows and repeated, "I'm Mr. Reed. Are you talking to me?"

I looked around, still startled and confused. Suddenly, the penny dropped. "Oh, I get it. Your name is Mr. Reed. You thought I was talking to you. Sorry. I was just telling my little Cocker Daschund – her name is Mystery – umm, telling her to get back into the car."

The man, who identified himself as Mr. Reed, roared in laughter: "Oh, you were saying Damnit, Mystery – the dog – get back in the car, not Damnit, Mr. Reed and cursing my name." Bob Reed roared and wheezed and laughed again. He lit a cigarette, inhaled deeply, coughed and exhaled with satisfaction. He pointed to my car and continued, "Hey, let me tell you something old boy. Don't you park that old piece of junk next to Cap'n Tobey's when you go to town in the morning?"

I nodded.

"Right across from Straight Wharf?"

"Yes, I do," I agreed. "Since there is little traffic in the early morning, I usually park just outside the Straight Wharf Tavern and walk up to the post office to get my mail, pick up a newspaper at the Hub – you know – run a few errands. But how did you know?"

Mystery poked her head out of the rear window frame as Bob Reed gave her a casual pat on the head.

"I know because I have coffee on that Wharf every morning on Gibby Nickerson's fishing boat. It's tied up directly across from The Tavern. We sit on his deck most mornings, drink coffee and watch the world go by.

"Well, my boy," he continued, "I can't tell you how many times we've watched you park that old rattletrap right across the street from us next to The Tavern. We watch you get out and we can actually hear you saying to your little dog, "Stay here. I'll be back in 30 minutes."

"Am I right?" said Mr. Reed.

"You are indeed," I said, wondering where this was going.

"Well," said Mr. Reed, "As soon as you're out of sight, and believe me she watches you into the distance, she flies out of that blown out window and trots over our way. Sometimes I give her a little crumb cake and Gibby throws her a small chunk of blue fish," Mr. Reed chuckled and continued. "And then she patrols the Wharf, occasionally allowing herself to be petted or fed by other fools like me ... Anyway, you say you usually take about 30 minutes with your errands?"

I nodded again.

"She does too – but she's always looking over her shoulder to your car and she continues to check up and down that old cobblestone Main Street until she sees you coming – and believe me, she sees you before you see her."

"How do you know?" I was a little confused.

"Because Gibby's boat is anchored maybe ten yards from where you park your car. Mystery provides a great source of entertainment. Hell, sometimes we wager how long before the 'little one' will spot you and fly back into the car, you none the wiser ... we've seen her do it a dozen times. It's so amusing to watch her jump back in the car just before you get there, and then we can actually hear you tell her what a good dog she is."

Mr. Reed looked at me with a big grin on his face to make sure I knew the joke was on me. I did.

"And how about that, you named her after me, eh? ... well sort of." Mr. Reed offered another of his wheezy laughs. Then he said, "Now that I know your dog's name, you might as well tell me yours."

"Joe Norton," I offered.

"Okay, Norton. I own this place." Mr. Reed made a sweeping gesture at the somewhat disjointed structure known as the Chicken Box. "All of it," he said. "The restaurant, the pool tables, the dance hall — even this lot where you park your car at night. You and your dog sort of amuse me. And I'm betting I can offer you a better job than what you are doing over at Finast. I've seen you working and sampling at the deli a number of times. Overall, I think you do a pretty good job there and, lucky for you, I'm a little short of staff at the moment. I could probably use you to do some work for me — right now. Come on in," he said, pointing to the restaurant door, while pausing to cough and spit out some phlegm on the ground. I was in deep sympathy for his lungs, but none of it seemed to bother Mr. Reed.

"Look, Norton, I can see for myself that you're tired, you're thirsty, and I'm sure you're sick of deli meat. Maybe this was providence intervening — Mystery's providence. Come on in the house and we'll talk about it."

He was right. I was tired of working at the deli and I needed something to kick me out of my growing fear that the gluey blue demons of depression were coming to get me.

"Does that include a drink?" I asked.

"Several," allowed Mr. Reed. "And a little kibble for Mystery, too."

Robert and Mr. Reed

## THE LEGEND OF THE CHICKEN BOX BAR,
## GRILL AND DANCE CLUB

My transition from the Finast deli to full-time helper/bartender at the Chicken Box went well enough. The Finast deli manager said he was tired of seeing me eat up the profits anyway and it turned out there was lots for me to do at the Box.

Mr. Reed hired me at the Chicken Box, thanks to Mystery in part. "I like the dog and I like you," he said. "My first instincts rarely let me down ... you're hired. Have another beer. You don't start until tomorrow. Now I'm going to give you a little history of the Chicken Box. That way you'll know a little bit more about me and Sid Carroll and Robert.

"Okay, sit tight and I'll tell you the story."

As I remember Mr. Reed's history lesson, this is how he came to own the Box.

Mr. Reed had a small company building houses one by one. In fact, he was largely a one-man building operation.

Sid Carroll was a much-lauded Weymouth High School football player but, with no college scholarships, he had nowhere to go after high school graduation. When he came looking for work, Mr. Reed agreed to train him as an apprentice carpenter but when he observed Sid's quick learning abilities and his steady work ethic, he gradually elevated him to a junior partnership and a full-time salary. Since it had always been Bob Reed doing everything his contract workers didn't, and he liked it that way, this was quite a commitment.

Sid never let him down. They became very close, almost a father and son relationship. Together they were able to accelerate the workload and, with lots of overtime, they completed a significant number of houses. Home construction was a booming economy in those days and they made a very good profit.

Although Sid had a long-term steady girlfriend, when he heard that Mr. Reed was planning a new building project on the Island of Nantucket, he was eager to sign on.

Mr. Reed remembered the conversation well and he shared it with me one day at the Box. 'Oh, you don't want to leave your girl and go over there,' he said to Sid. 'And I can get local help in Nantucket. They won't be as good as you, but I'll make out. As for you, you can just continue our business here in Weymouth. I'll back you financially and you'll do great."

"Wait a minute, Mr. Reed," Sid had said. "Maybe I do want 'in' on this Nantucket thing. And I like working with you and for you. So, tell me about it."

"Well," Mr. Reed had said slowly, "it sure would be easier if I had someone I could trust. Okay, let me describe this venture. If you still want in, we'll work something out."

Mr. Reed described the dream he'd had ever since he had seen Nantucket on a little day tripper cruise he had taken with his wife ten years before.

"As soon as we got off the boat, we took a bicycle ride out from Town Centre. We were headed east towards the little village of Siasconset about six miles away," he told Sid.

"Just a few miles outside of Nantucket Centre, I noticed all this undeveloped land in a small area I later learned was called Tom Nevers Way.

It led right down to the ocean a quarter mile away. Nothing was happening there so I wondered if the land could be bought and, if so, was it buildable and could a house building license be bought.

"Amazingly, my wife, who had rarely been out of Weymouth, MA where she was born, actually loved the idea of moving to Nantucket and living on this beautiful little isle 30 miles out to sea. This motivated me to explore all the local avenues to secure building permits and local financing for the land I wanted to build on. There were many hurdles in the coming months but I realized after doing all the necessary research and securing financing that I could probably pull it all off.

"Then my wife got liver cancer, and everything but the fight to save her life was put on hold. It was a long tough battle, but my wife was a fighter. She was cheerful and hopeful, but it was finally over in about two years. In my grief, I put the Nantucket dream aside and continued to focus on building locally. It was all I knew and, for a long time it was all my grief would allow me to do."

"I guess that's when I met him," said Sid, who had been listening right along with me. "And, I think that's when he started talking about Nantucket again. Of course, I wanted to go when he said he was ready to pursue that dream again."

Bob Reed continued. "Somehow, it all came together. First, we bought the land we wanted out Tom Nevers Way. It was cheap as no one seemed to want to live there. Too far out in the moor, they would say. But we, the two of us, saw the future. One by one, we built the houses and sold them to bring in the money to build more. Within three years, we had built a lot of houses, some custom but all complying with the simple salt box construction as was common in Nantucket. We made a lot of money.

"About that time, we found this place tucked away on the outskirts of Nantucket Centre."

*Buying the Place from Willie House*

The Chicken Box had originally been a "speak easy" bar/restaurant and chicken take out enterprise in 'Sconset all nurtured by the creative mind of Willie House. At some point he had moved the operation to the low rent outskirts of Nantucket Centre and added a dance hall. Over time and through Willie's connections, some famous blues singers, such as Muddy Waters, played there and both blues music and reggae became a part of the venue.

In the mid-70's, Willie was getting tired of running the business and that's when he met Bob Reed, who jumped at the chance to take it over.

"It was something I always wanted to do," Reed said, "but just never had the opportunity. Now, with a little money in the bank and our construction business thriving, I met Willie at just the right time for both of us. I bought the Chicken Box from Willie with the understanding that I would keep the same philosophy and that he would always be welcome there and that it would be my pleasure to continue to consult with him about the food or bringing in new groups or anything else that he observed.

"Of course, I had my own ideas too. We renovated the whole place, the bar, the dance floor, the stage area, but we kept Willie's philosophy to cater to the locals and we continued to seek out blues bands and reggae and added some good rock and roll.

"We never paid them a lot, but we did provide full overnight accommodations in the cottage/sheds we built behind the bar. We cooked their meals, gave them a bar tab, and of course, offered all of Nantucket they could explore in their time off. It worked out pretty well.

"We expected various tourist groups would show up for the bands we offered, but really the whole idea was to cater to the locals. And that's what we wanted, as Willie did, a local club for Nantucketers, a place that they could enjoy year-round. As we soon discovered, the tourists and summer dwellers liked it almost as much. Something about a democracy of booze and pool, music and dancing, ... some burgers and chicken, fries and local vegetables ... and casual cool ... that everybody seemed to like. Always, we were a happy and boisterous crowd. The Chicken Box's working philosophy was stated on a neon sign which hung on the wall behind the bar. It said, *Be Nice or Get Out.*

"And that's just the way it turned out, fun, profitable and we've made a lot of friends. It's a great life. So now you know a little bit about how the

Chicken Box came together for us. And you may have come along at just the right time to become a part of it."

## *The Story of Robert*

The other full-time member of the Chicken Box triumvirate, when I signed on, was Robert Finley, 6'3," of coal black complexion, and about 300 pounds of muscle and carefully nurtured abundance. Legend has it, he was born and raised in Winston-Salem, North Carolina. That's where he was sent to jail for assaulting a white man who had cursed his girlfriend, Jessie, calling her a "little black bitch" when she hadn't gotten out of his way quick enough. Robert, who was standing just behind Jessie, grabbed the man by his neck, and lifted him off the ground with one hand and slapped him almost unconscious with the other. Southern justice being what it was, Robert was convicted of assault and battery and sentenced to a year in jail.

While Robert was in jail, Jessie was continually harassed by other whites because of the incident. She decided to leave Winston-Salem to go and live with her aunt right here on Nantucket. Before she left, she wrote Robert in jail to say she was sorry, that she still loved him, but she was moving to Nantucket Island, off the coast of Massachusetts, to start a new life. In her last note, she wrote that she wished him well and hoped he would find peace in his own life when he got out of jail.

Robert understood that this was a "Dear John" letter but, because he had never stopped loving her, when he got out of jail he decided to get on a Greyhound, go to Hyannis, Massachusetts and take the ferry over to Nantucket. Against the odds, Robert still hoped to win Jessie back.

When Robert arrived on Island, he walked straight over to Five Corners, which was the predominately black neighborhood just outside of Nantucket Centre. He was looking for his girl. He knocked on the screen door of a cottage where he had been told that Jessie was living. When she appeared, facing him from the other side of the screen door, Robert noticed that there was a man standing behind her. Jessie looked shocked to see Robert even as she invited him in.

With tears in her eyes, she introduced him to her fiancé who was standing behind her. "Robert, this is Johnny, and he is a part of my new life."

Robert smiled and shook hands with Johnny. "I was upset," said Robert, "but I didn't want to hurt nobody … but I felt bad … real bad."

After a little talk, and wishing him well, Jessie gave Robert a quick hug and opened the door for him to go.

"Yeah, I remember it pretty well," said Robert. "I walked a couple of blocks and I saw this sign. It said, 'Welcome to the Chicken Box.' I had nowhere to go so I just sat down on this tree stump in the parking lot. I hung my head and started to cry out loud. I ain't never done that before. I was completely empty. Everything was black and my head hurt so bad. That's when I really wished I was dead. And that's when this man showed up." Robert smiled and pointed to Mr. Reed. "He tapped me on the shoulder from behind. And as I turned slowly, he spoke to me."

"'A big man like you balling,'" Mr. Reed had said. "'It must have been pretty bad. Well, I want to talk to you. Listen, I can't have a big man like you crying out here in my parking lot. It'll scare the customers away. Come on in the house. I'll buy you a cup of coffee. And let's just talk about it. Come on. Get up. Let's go.'"

Robert continued. "Somehow, he just pulled me up and I followed him on in. He sat me down at this bar and looked me straight in the eye so that I could see that he was serious. And that's when I decided I probably should just shut my mouth and find out what he was all about."

Mr. Reed and Robert both laughed. Sid did, too. Then Mr. Reed picked up the story as Sid and I and Robert smiled attentively.

"Yeah, somehow I knew Robert was just the man we needed. I think I knew by instinct and just by talking with him that he was somebody I would want to know. He would fight back against a white man who had assaulted his woman even though he knew white man's justice would put him in jail for doing it. I knew by the way he followed her up to our Island to win her back and yet still had the grace to leave her alone when he knew she was happy with another man. He had the courage, the strength, and the heart to be the man I would want to work with Sid and me. And the fact that he could hold up that white racist with one hand and slap him around with the other, well, I figured that could come in pretty handy around here some nights."

"Yeah, I know," said Sid, chiming in. "A marriage made in heaven."

"Well, it was," said Robert. "I didn't have nowhere to go when I met Mr. Reed, and as my Daddy would say, 'I was feeling lower than a snake's belly,' when he found me. I owe him a lot."

"Shoot, Robert, we owe you!" said Mr. Reed. "Look what you've done for us since you signed on at the Chicken Box. You help us keep this place going. You keep it clean, you come early, you leave late, you're a great bouncer, and man, we needed that. And when I found out you could cook on a grill, things like burgers and fries and fish and all kinds of other fried stuff, that meant I no longer had to cook in the kitchen. You do it all, and at the end of a long night, after I count the day's "take," I know I can give it to you and be absolutely sure you will get it to the bank the next morning. Meanwhile, I can go home and get some sleep because, Robert, you're the only man I trust … err, with the possible exception of you, Sid," Mr. Reed said with a wink. "Yes, the only man I can trust with all the cash and receipts to make the deposit the next morning and bring it back to me when we open. When I give you that brown paper bag to take to the bank, I know I can trust you absolutely."

"Well, one thing for sure," said Robert smiling, "when you give that money to me at the end of the night, ain't nobody gonna take it from me until I walk it to the bank the next morning. Nobody! They'd have to kill me first."

"Yeah, and I don't think anyone in his right mind would want to try that," said Sid.

All four of us laughed at the prospect. Mr. Reed turned to me once more with that wry grin. "I don't know how we ended up with this reprobate," he said pointing at me, "but something tells me our resident writer-waiter and former deli boy is gonna work out just fine." I noticed he still had a bread crumb lodged in his scraggly beard, probably from the sandwich he had recently consumed. He continued with a twinkle in his eye and said, "All right, Norton. If you don't mind, would you go get me a root beer."

I knew Mr. Reed didn't drink alcohol anymore, something he had said 'Every man has to deal with alcohol in his own way and I didn't like what it was doing to me so I just stopped.'

I responded to his request accordingly. "Oh, no, sir," I said, jumping up from my stool and bowing deeply before him. "How would Mr. Reed like that served, in a frosty mug or should I just bring a pre-opened bottle?"

"Just bring me a mug," said Mr. Reed, evenly.

"All right, sir, now, would you like it to come with just a little bit of foam or gushing over the top?"

"How 'bout I kick your ass over the top of this bar?"

"Okay, so I'll just bring it with a modicum of foam," I said, smiling. Right about this time I dodged Mr. Reed's approaching kick towards my derriére. I left the group smiling and came back with his root beer.

"Too much foam," he said, "but I like the substance," he said, staring at me.

"Now sit down, my boy. Have another Molson on the house. I've got the next episode for you. It's the story of Robert and the brawl at the bar."

At this point, Robert got up, smiling and shaking his head, and went out to the parking lot to clean up the remains of last night.

"Robert is a little bit shy about all this praise I heap upon him, but he deserves it and it needs to be told."

"When we finished renovating the Box in August of '77 and when the first mainland band arrived here in late September, we had no idea what kind of crowds we would draw. But as the word got around about the live bands, the crowds began to grow. It was hard to keep up. It turned out we needed Robert more than we ever dreamed.

"Robert was doing everything he could to help us make it all work out, from cooking to cleaning up, taking the money at the door, and, when necessary, being a bouncer. It had been a beautiful fall and an unusually warm October. There were still lots of weekenders who swelled the usual Islander clientele. But, many of the other bar/restaurant night clubs had closed for the season, and a lot of their customer base began coming to us. We began to have large Friday and Saturday night crowds. Sometimes 30 to 40 people would be lined up outside the admission door waiting to get in." (Now remember, this is the same Robert who kept the place clean every day, who helped cook on the grill, and who received the day's "take" at the end of every night so that he could deposit it at the Pacific National Bank the next morning.)

"You know, Norton, I didn't know exactly what I would do with Robert when I first took him on, but man, like osmosis and that smile on his face, he just evolved into being everything we needed to make the operation work.

'You my family now,' Robert told me, 'and I take care of my family.'

"Well, you sure have been family to me," said Bob Reed, smiling.

"Anyway, back on that particular Saturday night of October 1977 …"

"Wait a minute," said Sid Carroll, who was dolly-rolling a keg of Narragansett beer across the floor. He stopped the dolly and leaned over the keg for a moment, and said, "Are you tellin' that biker brawl story again?"

"Well, I was beginning to," said Mr. Reed.

"Well, I wanna hear that one again," said Sid. "Remember, I was with you. I saw what happened. But I gotta say, Mr. Reed, you sure have a way of telling that story a little differently every time I hear it." Turning to me, Sid said, "Norton, you're gonna love this. Nobody tells a better bar yarn than Mr. Reed, and no one is a better bouncer than Robert, and I've seen 'em all."

Sid parked his tall lanky frame on a stool next to mine, after first leaving the keg and dolly on the floor and grabbing a cold beer from the cooler behind the bar. "Break time, Bob Reed. I want to hear your 'Robert the Bouncer' story one more time."

Mr. Reed, still standing, leaned over the bar from the other side. He nodded to us and began anew. "Okay, boys, here's how I remember it tonight … and I've only been drinking root beer."

About this time Robert came back inside and said, "Oh, Lord, I don't need to hear that one again. I think I'll just go on into the kitchen and set up the grill for tonight."

Robert slipped through the swinging door into the kitchen as Mr. Reed called after him. "Oh, right, Robert. I forgot; you are now the chief cook around here. When you first came here you were the chief cleaning person. Pretty soon you became the chief in charge of money deposits… now, you're just about ready to take over the whole place."

"Maybe I is," said Robert, with his big smile, as he disappeared through the swinging door.

Mr. Reed turned back to Sid and me. "Probably could run the whole dang place," said Bob Reed.

"Incredible," said Sid, still sitting on the bar stool to my right. He reached over the bar to the cooler, pulled up a cold beer and handed it to me. I held it up to the light as if inspecting it for quality and quantity, popped it open and took a big swig.

"He loves this place – loves us," said Sid, "so when those local rednecks showed up here one night in the fall of our first year, he was not going to let them mess with us or the Box. I remember what he said after that night's first incident was over after the brawl, 'Don't nobody mess with the Box. They's my family.'

"And that was before the actual biker brawl on that same night," said Sid.

"All right, Sid," said Mr. Reed. "I'll take over from here, my son."

"You always do, Big Daddy," said Sid, laughing. "Please proceed."

Bob Reed took a large sip from his mug of root beer and clinked its side to the bottle of beer that Sid held. "Ah, where was I, Norton?" said Mr. Reed, winking at me.

"Okay, Norton, remember, this is a two-part story. Let me set the scene for the first event of that night. It was late November. But even in that short time, Robert had become invaluable to the operation … almost as valuable as you, Sid, whom I love and respect – mostly – and while I do not know much about you, Norton – too early to tell – still, I've got my hopes."

I coughed slightly as Mr. Reed now clinked my beer. "Okay, drink up you two reprobates, and I'll continue. As I said, it was crisp and cold on that night but we had a really hot blues/rock band that had developed a big following in Boston and the Cape. Sid knew one of the band members from high school and they all thought it would be really cool to come over here and play at the Box and then have the whole day to run around the Island. It was a seven-piece band, with brass, guitars, drums, bitchin' piano playing, and raspy cool vocals. They called themselves Spider and the Tangled Web. I caught their act in Boston before I booked them. They were amazing. They had the whole crowd stompin' and cheerin' and there was lots of dancing going on … our kind of band."

*Bar Room Brawl*

"Well, here's how I describe that night's events, Norton," said Mr. Reed. "I call it Robert's Concerto and the Nantucket Chicken Box Brawl.

"It was like a two-act play, the first were requests, followed by insults, minor threats, and Robert's instant retribution. The second part was a separate incidence of gathering threats, which led to lightening quick violence, followed by the satisfaction of island justice and resolution.

"Okay," said Mr. Reed. "It was a beautiful, cold Saturday night at the Box with this incredible band, Spider and the Tangled Web – I just love that name. Anyway, there was a long line waiting to get in to see them. On this particular night, as I was saying, two local drunk punks were at the head of the line, waiting to pay the cover. As usual, Robert was 'at the door' and, apparently, these particular locals thought they could talk their way past him."

"Come on, Robert," one of them said. 'We don't care about this crummy band. We just want to come in for a couple of drinks before we head on home.' Billy Baker, as he was known, became loud and insistent. He began jabbing his finger against Robert's chest to make his point. Robert finally decided he'd had enough. According to a fellow standing in line just behind Billy Baker, Robert grabbed the offending finger and bent it backwards as its owner screamed in pain. Then he literally grabbed both of the offenders by the scruff of their necks with his giant hands and tree trunk arms, and shoved them off into the darkness, saying, 'You boys can come back when you're ready to pay the cover.'

"As he was stumbling away, Billy was heard to yell, 'Well, we're gonna come back, Robert, and you'll be sorry when we do.' The crowd in line hooted and hollered at Billy and his buddy as they jumped in their truck and drove away.

"Norton, you know, we actually didn't think they would come back that night," said Mr. Reed. "They were just punks, nasty punks to be sure, but we figured they would just go off to their homes, sleep it off and try and come back another night. But they did come back about 45 minutes later. And they were joined by six biker types from off Island. Billy said he wanted us to meet his six new buddies that he had met in town.

"With a sly grin, Billy said he was truly sorry about before, and that

Big Joe had offered to pay the cover for everybody in his group. Billy pointed in the general direction of a large black-bearded fellow wearing a leather jacket and some kind of heavy chain hanging from his neck. Big Joe stepped forward and handed Robert a $100 bill, saying, 'Let's see - $10 cover, eh? That's $80 for the whole group, including our two local friends, and a $20 tip for you. Keep the change, Boy.'

Mr. Reed rubbed his chin and continued his story. "Robert took the $100 bill, examined it, and slowly opened the door to let the group pass through. He then told the waiting crowd he would be right back. He locked the door and slipped up to me.

"Robert bent his head toward mine and spoke so that only I could hear him. 'Those little skitter bugs came back and they brough back those bike boys over there with them. I think they is trouble, Mr. Reed.' Then Robert returned to his place at the door.

Grinning at me, Mr. Reed drew in a long breath. "About this time, Big Joe pushed his way through the crowd to the bar and began talking in my general direction. Big Joe pretended not to know I was the owner though he did, and even as I knew he was the 'leader of the pack.' First he complained about how their motorcycles were confiscated in Hyannis earlier that night, just because they did a few wheelies in the town square. But now he said, 'We're just lookin' for a good time and a few good women. You got any good time women around here, old man?' Then Big Joe pointed toward Robert and said, 'Our local pals here had a pretty tough time with your Boy over there earlier tonight. You are the owner, right, old man?' I remember nodding my head, slowly as Big Joe continued, 'I think he's pretty uppity for a crash and trash kind of place like this. Hey, we've trashed lots better places than this, ain't we, boys?' The other bikers, who had by now elbowed their way to the front of the bar, laughed loudly.

"It was at this point that I whispered to Sid, 'Go to the phone in the kitchen and call Chief Tom Boublais. Tell him to get the cops down here, ASAP! All hell is gonna break loose here any moment.' I reached under the bar across from Big Joe and grabbed my billy club so that he could not see it. I nodded to Robert, who locked the front door and moved behind the bar next to me.

"In the meantime, Big Joe, warming to his audience, continued to escalate his tirade as if he were looking for a fight and didn't really care if the cops came or not. It turned out later, he didn't; he and his biker boys had no place to spend the night and he must have figured the comforts of jail would be just as good as lying out on the cold beach somewhere. Besides, the cops would probably give them breakfast before kicking them out of town the next morning.

'Hell, what's your name, ... Mr. Reed? You say you own this dump, right?' I smiled at Big Joe but it wasn't a friendly smile. 'Yes, I do, Mr. ... err ... Big Joe, is it? If the Chicken Box is not up to your usual standards, I'll be happy to refund the cover charge and you and your group of 'fellow travelers' can go somewhere else."

'Shit, no, old man. I'm just startin' to have a good time. This music sucks but I've heard worse. The women don't look like much but that's okay, too. I ain't choosy. The only thing that pisses me off is that Boy right there,' he said as he pointed at Robert, 'actin' like he owns the place. Why he ought to be in the john, cleaning toilets, when he ain't polishing shoes.'

"Now most nasty words don't bother me much," said Mr. Reed to us. "I can handle that kind of ignorance – but you don't mess with my family. And Robert is family. When you engage in ignorant racial slurs, that's a line you cannot cross in the Chicken Box, and when you're laying it out on Robert, who is family, that's when it becomes, how should I put this ... unacceptable."

"I leaned in across the bar so that my face was about two inches from Big Joe's. 'You know, Big Joe,' I said, 'you've been lookin' for a good time and I believe you deserve it. I hope you get a kick out of this.' With that, I pulled my billy club from under the bar and proceeded to slam it against the side of Big Joe's head, methodically, once, twice, and a third time. It seemed to do the trick. Joe's eyes went vacant as he slowly crumbled to the floor. I noticed that Big Joe's entourage were shocked, frozen in place. It was the suddenness of it all. Before they had time to react, Robert moved in with both fists pile driving. Meanwhile, Sid, who had completed his call to the police, broke a cue stick over the head of one man and waded in with fists flying against another. By this time, a number of enthusiastic

Nantucket locals had isolated the remaining bikers and were basically beating the crap out of them.

"You know, Norton," said Mr. Reed, "it was amazing how quickly it was over. It doesn't take long for violence to make its mark. Ours was quicker, faster, and more directed than any of those biker boys, and by the time all the other locals jumped into the fracas, the change of heart in those fellows was dramatic, from 'nasty and tough' to begging for mercy."

Mr. Reed smiled broadly as he lurched to the conclusion of the great Chicken Box Bar Room Brawl.

"Well, right about then, Chief Boublais came running through the door with about five deputies huffing and puffing behind him, only to find six bikers already sprawled on the floor in various conditions of distress. There were about twenty Box people standing over them. I remember there was a kind of taunting going on by Robert who was shaking his fist at one of the bikers, 'Looks like you 'ol biker boys just hit the skids. Now you all better just lay there 'til the cops get here or we Chicken Box people might have to beat you up all over again.'

"Sid had also added his thoughts to this theme," said Mr. Reid, something like, 'Yeah, Robert, I wouldn't want to waste another cue stick breaking it over their heads again.'"

Bob Reed continued, "And, then, Chief Tom Boublais broke into the conversation, 'All right, all right, we've got it boys. You can step back now.' I remember the deputies glared down at the humbled bikers. 'Dang it,' said Deputy Coleman Bigelow, tapping his baton against his knee. 'I had to give up my Saturday night to clean up this mess you clowns have made. You'd better not piss me off anymore.'"

'Hey, Coleman,' said the Chief. 'A little decorum, please. I'm sure these gentlemen know they have made a few wrong choices tonight, and that is how they ended up in such a pitiful condition.'

"Big Joe, of the bikers, rolled over on his hip in order to raise his hand and say something, but the Chief immediately pushed out his own hand as if to make it a stop sign. 'Big fella, you don't wanna say anything just yet. Your best chance is to just get kicked off the Island without spending some time in jail for being drunk and disorderly, and I can see you were,' this as the

Chief pointed to broken chairs, beer bottles, the odd orphan sock and shoe and various other forms of debris. 'Yes, I can see that you were drunk and disorderly. So, shut your mouth until I decide what's best for all concerned. Do you understand me?' Big Joe dropped his hand and simply cradled the left side of his head where Bob Reed had hit him with the billy club so methodically and efficiently just a few minutes before. Then Joe pointed weakly at me and said words to the effect to the Chief that I had tried to kill him. Can you imagine that? Me. Big Teddy Bear, Bob Reed."

" 'Well, obviously he didn't succeed – you're still breathing,' said Chief Boublais. Then the chief turned to Deputy Andrews and said, 'Make sure Joe doesn't interrupt me while I talk to Mr. Reed.'

"It was at this point that we realized that Billy and his pal were nowhere to be seen," said Bob Reed.

"They must have run off when the brawl broke out," said Sid. "Now that gives our locals a bad name."

Mr. Reed laughed heartily and continued. "Meanwhile, Deputy Skinner Andrews stood over Joe, holding his truncheon in hand. 'Gladly, Chief,' and then to Joe, 'This is called a truncheon, Big Joe, and it really could kill you.'

"At this, Joe went radio silent, sullen but silent.

"Chief Tom Boublais listened as I gave him a summary of that night's series of events from the initial confrontation with Robert by the two locals, their eviction and subsequent return with the six bikers, all primed and ready for combat."

" 'Well, they might have been primed,' said Chief Boublais, 'but they obviously weren't ready. I mean look at this roadkill,' pointing to the still sprawled bikers.

"The Chief laughed at his own description and then continued, 'Okay, Mr. Reed, what do you want me to do with them?'

"Nothing," I said to the Chief.

"They got their comeuppance. I just don't want to see them in here again … ever. And you might want to consider getting them off the Island entirely. I think they might just cause more problems – might even try to get back in here again."

'Gotcha,' said the Chief. 'I'll just give 'em a free night in jail with all the fixin's. Hell, I'll even give them breakfast tomorrow morning and a one-way ticket on the 7 a.m. ferry to Hyannis. But first I will explain to Joe that the alternative to not accepting this generous offer would be a series of misdemeanor charges which could keep them in jail for quite a long time.'

"The Chief now looked over in the direction of Joe, who had been listening to the entire proceedings, he continued. 'So, Joe, do you want to do this the easy way, that is my way, so that you can get your tails out of here on the morning boat to Hyannis and continue your manly quest to get your motorcycles back? Or do you choose the hard way, in which case I will throw the book at you?'

"There was barely a pause when Joe was heard to say quietly, 'You got me. I'll take door number 1. We just want to get our bikes back and get the hell back to Bayonne. Hell, I wish we'd never left New Jersey.'

'Excellent choice, Big Joe,' said the Chief. 'Tomorrow, this episode will be a mere blip on the radar, barely a record to be made of it. That's good for the Box and that's good for you, Joe. But remember, you guys just got lucky.'

"Chief Boublais turned to his deputies. 'All right, boys, round 'em up and get 'em in the paddy wagon. Next stop free jail accommodations for one night only and a free one-way ticket for all of them back to Hyannis.' The Chief turned back to Joe one last time. 'By the way, if any of you ever come back to Nantucket and the Chicken Box, I will charge you with criminal trespassing. That's a felony and you will rot in jail. Do not come back. You are not welcome. Return at your own peril. Got it? All right, deputies, get them out of here.'"

"Wow," I said at this dramatic and clever conclusion.

"Wow is right," said Sid Carroll. "Mr. Reed is smart — but Chief Boublais was even smarter in the way he handled this group and protected the 'civil' reputation of the Chicken Box. No black eye for the Chicken Box, no further disturbance in Nantucket Centre, and the bikers were cleanly evicted, never to return, no muss, no fuss. It was almost as if they were never here, except for the legend that grew from the supposed events of that night."

"And did Joe and his boys ever get their motorcycles back?" I inquired.

"Who the hell cares?" said Mr. Reed. "But I know they never came back. And I know it was a legendary night for the Box which gave us major awareness up and down the Cape. It kinda put us on the map. The group that played that night even created a song for us. It actually helped the bookings, especially since everything turned out for the best," said Bob Reed.

"Well, what was the name of the song?" I asked.

"*Robert's Concerto.*"

"Really?" I said.

"Really," said Bob Reed, slowly.

"Now, have another beer."

"Really?" I said.

"Really," he said, pulling out his billy club from under the bar and brandishing it in my direction. "This is what I used during the barroom brawl," Mr. Reed smiled.

"Would you like a demonstration?"

"Err, no, sir."

"Really?" said Mr. Reed evenly.

"Really'" I said. "And I'll never use that word again."

"Really," said Mr. Reed.

"For sure," I said.

Even then I could hear Robert in the kitchen chuckling at the rekindling of the great biker barroom brawl at the Chicken Box. He knew it was coming, and so did I.

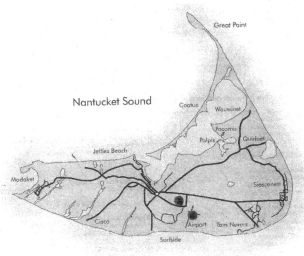

*Robert's Concerto* was memorialized in poetry by a writer/ patron of The Chicken Box some years later. Here it is:

I need to get in man. I'm having a spree
It's late. I ain't danced, so let me in free
I live on this Island and I'm holding some gin
Oh Robert, friend Robert, you must let me in.

You ain't nuthin, less'n you pay at dis door
Jus' show me two dollars, nothin less, nothin more
An' then you gets in, for the rest of the dance
But don't mess wid me, you pays for your chance.

Hey Robert, you're savvy, I know where you've been
I ain't got no money, but I'll give you some gin
I got you covered, I know who's been down
Don't mess with me, I gut friends all around.

Well, I'm telling you dis, and I'm telling you cool
You ain't nuthin' to me, but a jive-turkey fool
If'n you gut the dollars, you'll have a ball
And if'n you ain't, man, get ready to fall.

The foregoing was published in Bob Reed's Nantucket NITE LIFE in 1982. Bob Reed described the circumstances accordingly:

*"The foregoing was submitted by writer Alden Bigelow of Charlottesville, N.C. He spent a good part of '78 here and is threatening to pay us a visit come summer. Is Nantucket up to harboring fugitive celebrities?"*

## NANTUCKET WINTER WATERMAN BLUES

The Tavern, looking over the basin of the harbor, looks out on the only marina on the island. It was a welcoming nightcap place I would go after finishing my waitering/bartending duties at the Chicken Box Bar, Grille, Nightclub. I would drive downtown and leave Mystery, my trusty black cocker mongrel, to guard, preserve, and protect our car until I got back.

It was cold and the fog had already rolled in on this late evening of December 20, 1978 on the Island of Nantucket.

I spotted Eric and Gerry across the room as I entered the Tavern. They were seated at a slightly tattered red leather corner booth, the victims of a long summer season. They had two Heinekens placed on the white Formica tabletop in front of them. A number of empties were lined up on the window sill beside them, supposedly just to keep count. Obviously, they had been here for awhile. They waved at me exuberantly as I came over to join them.

"Hey, get on over here you big old landlubber," said Eric. "You're way behind on your beer count."

Eric was a compact, sinewy muscular figure with black, darting eyes, blond short cropped hair, chiseled features and feet that would incessantly tap the floor as he sat back to tell you his latest story.

His friend and fellow coxswain, Gerry, was almost by contrast tall, angular, and easygoing. A demeanor of laid back, fluid moves. He would laugh indulgently at yet another one of Eric's yarns.

As for me, I saw Nantucket for what it was, an island of dreams, of grace and redemption, thirty miles off the coast of Massachusetts, barely thirteen miles long and four miles across at its widest point.

And so, once again, there we were at the Tavern as we had been nearly every night since the "summer dwellers" had left at the end of September.

In season, the Tavern on the Straight Wharf overlooked 50 million dollars' worth of dories and sailboats, fishing boats and whalers, thirty-foot sloops with sleeping accommodations for eight, Criscraft "stink pots" with the Lily Pulitzer floating living rooms and gin palaces, and finally, the multi-million dollar ocean crossing hundred-foot ships with a large standing crew and a chef on-call at all times.

All these boats represented the major workload in the summer season for the Nantucket Coast Guard. As two of the premier coxswains, Eric and Gerry were an integral part of this process.

Their job was to certify, regulate, and all too often, rescue these weekend sailors who, for various reasons, violated the rules of the water. There were those who never ventured out of the society and safety of the harbor slip except for the occasional drunk who fell or was knocked overboard.

As for those skippers who would venture out of Nantucket Harbor, they were in open ocean in which they could theoretically motor or sail three thousand miles clear until they reached Spain.

Far more likely was the boating which occurred within ten miles of Nantucket Harbor. Here is where the mishaps, hijinks and catastrophes occurred from which the Nantucket Coast Guard would rescue them. Eric and Gerry were usually on a 21 foot Harbor Craft which could accommodate most of these mishaps.

Even as I began to listen to their stories of the season, I realized that they were themselves an integral part of the Nantucket lore. This tiny little

Island whose whaling industry inspired Herman Melville to write Moby Dick in which supports a hardcore native and year round population of barely 7,000 will swell to 50,000 in the summer season. That is the season of the summer dwellers who come to live for a few months in their multi-million dollar oceanfront compounds, or those who rented the charming saltbox, grey shingled cottages at exorbitant rates.

Then there are the young people, the student summer workers at the yacht club or the innumerable waiters and waitresses and bartenders such as myself who support the impossibly short, but immeasurably lucrative, restauranting business in high season.

Many are here to earn money for their college fall semester, while for others, such as myself, it was to make enough just to live here. And then there were the rich kids who hung out at the yacht club and played tennis and sailed out in their day sailers. And then there was the boating crowd of yachts all moored and jammed into their boating slips at the marina just below the Tavern, where we were on that early winter night.

We all came for the magic, the money and the parties, the daily beach nights and the fishing and the food and quite a few professional drinkers. All were tolerated on this magical island.

Now all of that was over until next year. The summer dwellers had gone back to the real world of jobs and schedules, or else boated down the inland waterway to stay even with the warmth of the sun.

We would begin to miss them as the winter deepened and we would certainly miss the commerce and other summertime enjoyment they brought, but it was good to be to ourselves, even as we considered the vaguries of the coming of winter.

"Hey, Norton – where's your head been at? I just bought you a Molson to get you in the mood."

I smiled, grabbed the long neck and chugged it. I figured I better get ready for the coming of Eric's sea stories. Eric raised his hand and snapped his fingers, which almost immediately produced a waiter with three more beers – "Norton, I told him to give you good service. I told him you're writing a story about us (*I wasn't at the time*). Anyways, I wanna keep you lubricated to put you in the mood – are you feeling it?"

"Well, I am getting there. If I'm gonna write a story about you guys, you better give me some good material."

"Oh, we've got the material, Norton," said Gerry. "Eric, why don't you tell Norton a little bit about our summer season."

And so it began.

"You remember the fool who sailed his ketch out of the harbor and into the blue, despite red flag warnings?" said Eric. "He capsized a quarter-mile past Coatue. God, we picked him up bobbing like a wine cork in a water trough. We pulled him in even as our boat was taking on enough water to swamp it in that weather. And all the little bastard would say was, 'If you Coast Guard pricks would have gotten here sooner, you could've saved my yacht.' God, Norton, I should've dropped him back in the water."

"Yeah, without his life jacket," laughed Gerry.

"Hey, remember that couple we picked up swimming in the ocean near Shimmo?" said Gerry.

"Seems like they carefully anchored their boat to nothing but water as they dropped off the boat for an afternoon dip. 'The boat just drifted off and we couldn't swim back to it' they said. 'So then we thought we could just swim back to shore and get a lift from some sailing buddies to come back and rescue it.' "

"Good plan, only would've taken you a long time to swim there, given the fact of the direction in which you were swimming," said Eric.

'Why do you say that?' said the woman, 'we are very good swimmers.'

"Maybe so," said Gerry slowly. "Only in the direction you were going it would have taken you an awfully long time to get there."

'Why is that?' persisted the woman.

"Because, ma'am," Gerry said, "you were swimming due east to Spain, that's about a three-thousand mile swim." Laughter all around.

"Yeah, that was pretty funny," said Gerry. "That woman just glared at her husband all the way back into the harbor. They still weren't speaking later on as we got their boat back to them."

"I guess she figured he should have kept swimming to Spain." laughed Gerry.

"If I had been married to her I might've tried," said Eric.

"Okay, here's one more for you, Norton," said Eric.

"I call it the Black Lab Rescue. You won't believe it. It was the middle of the day, blue skies, cool breeze, no rescue calls— just our usual inspection tour we carried out throughout the harbor."

"Suddenly just beyond Couteau, we spotted a woman screaming from her yacht, arms up and waving frantically to get our attention. Apparently, her black lab had jumped off the bow of the boat in its exuberance to catch a low flying seagull. We could see him treading water, but the woman said every time she would try to swim to him he would swim off. Even then we could see the dog was confused and frightened. It was just a matter of time before she would grow too weak, would swallow water and drown. At first we weren't quite sure what to do. Then, Eric cut off a long piece of rope and fashioned a noose at the end of it. Norton, I know what you're thinking – he was gonna try to lasso the dog. Nope, too difficult and he might've strangled the dog. What he did do was throw the rope as close to the dog as he could where it began to bob up and down in the water. Ever so slowly, as Eric began to pull the rope in. The dog immediately spotted it and instinct took over, he swam to the noose and grabbed it firmly between his teeth as if he were retrieving a bird his master had just shot. The rope stayed clenched and Eric drew the dog and the rope alongside the boat. I jumped in and pushed the dog up the side of our rescue boat and Eric pulled him in. Darla, as we came to know her, jumped all over us in her gratefulness, gave us both big licks, then we motioned her miss to follow us into the harbor in her day sailer. We tied up and walked Darla over to Katie, her mistress. She was all smiles and Darla was extremely happy. Smothering her with kisses. Of course, Katie was grateful and wanted to give us a tip, which we immediately declined."

"So, what happened next?" I wanted to know.

"Well, let's see…" said Eric.

"First, Katie insisted on buying us a drink when we got off work. Gerry said, no thanks. I said, yes please."

"And then?" I asked.

Eric looked down and smiled but he did not want to talk about it.

"It was a brief encounter," Gerry said. "That's all Eric would tell me."

"Now you've got to tell us," Gerry said. "Norton's the writer. He will want to know. Was it a one night stand?"

"No," said Eric, laughing. " You can be so crude, Gerry. You have no sense of romance." And then there was that sly smile on his face. "Okay, it was a five-day romance. Then she and Darla had to go home to the mainland."

"And your heart was broken?" asked Gerry.

"Well, Katie was a great, great girl… but I think I'll miss Darla the most." There was a big grin on his face.

Abruptly the conversation shifted.

Eric said he hated the off-season. "Too much to think about in the off-season without the adrenaline rush of the summer rescues. I just got a letter from my ex-wife. She says she's gonna move out of Massachusetts and up to Vermont. I think she's got a boyfriend up there and I don't have a problem with any of that. I certainly trust her with my six-year-old son, but I'm never gonna get up there to see him. My ex says I'm welcome to see little Mikey any time I can get up there so I can't complain, but it will sure be a pain in the ass getting up there and I'm not going to be able to go until next year, and even then I won't have enough time to drive him down here to the Island and get him back to Vermont."

"Wait a minute, Eric. You can take time off to get him and bring him on down next spring. You've got plenty of leave time."

"Yeah, I guess I could," said Eric. "Yeah, maybe I will. I do love my kid after all, but you know I'm only at peace when I am on the water, even when it's rescuing that little shit on the ketch, and especially when I was rescuing Darla, the black lab. Yeah, it's always the water that brings me back to myself."

There was a short silence. Then Eric lifted his beer in toast. "Here's to the Mother ocean. May we never be too far away from her."

Then suddenly Eric pushed himself out of the booth and stood up. "Well, I think I've had enough." he said quietly. "I think I'll go on back to the station and get some shut eye."

"Okay, Eric," Gerry said, reaching out to shake his hand. "I hope you aren't too drunk to walk home."

Eric almost whispered, "Hell, the station is only a five minute walk away. I could crawl there from here."

"Good idea," said Gerry. "You might be safer that way."

Eric backed out the door, pointed his finger at us with that same big, enigmatic smile and said, "Who knows, I might just get lucky."

"He's pretty lit," said Gerry. "But, as you know, the station is just around the corner. He'll probably go home and sleep it off — get up feeling fresh as a daisy, while I'll be in a hungover haze with a headache that will take half a day to get rid of. You don't have to worry about Eric, he will be fine."

Gerry and I left the Tavern together, said our goodbyes and I headed back to my rattletrap car, where my impatient Mystery was now wagging her tail in forgiveness.

I gave her a quick pet and we drove home to our cottage by the pond. All in all it had been a pretty good night.

When I returned to the Tavern a few nights later I hoped Gerry and Eric would be there to greet me. I saw Gerry sitting at that same tattered booth in the corner, but no Eric. Gerry saw me. Still he seemed to be looking right past me as if hoping to see someone else come in from the darkness of the harbor.

I sat down across from him.

"Eric is gone," he whispered. "Gone back to the water, and this time he'll stay."

"Eric never got back when he left us the other night." Gerry lifted his glass of beer, took a long swallow and exhaled deeply. "I don't know why he did it but I've got a pretty good fix on how he did it."

I heard the past tense in Gerry's talk and started to say something. Gerry held up his hands as if to silence me.

"Norton, when Eric left I figured he'd walk around Children's Beach to Brant Point, take a right, and trot on down to the station 200 yards away. I figured he'd sleep off the booze and be as good as new the next morning. But he never got there.

"I've talked to the cops and heard what they know and since I know Eric better than most anybody else, I think I know what really happened.

"Yeah, just passing Children's Beach when he sees a canoe in the sand, must have come untethered and there it was all by itself on that beach. I figure Eric must have come up with one of his crazy ideas. He goes over to the canoe and sees it still has its paddle tucked inside and what happened next is pretty much what the police think too. We all know Eric on this small island, he must have said, 'What the hell? Why walk back to the station when I can paddle back in this beauty? I'll return it in the morning. The owner has probably gone back to Florida by now.' Anyway that's how the cops and I think Eric came to be in that canoe – a little midnight canoe dip in the harbor – what a hoot.

"Now, the cops say that Eric must have taken that canoe into the water and must have fell out because he was drunk and lost his balance. I think what happened is he stood up in the bow to howl at the moon, then lost his balance and fell out. The cops say he drowned because he couldn't swim to the shore in the freezing water; hypothermia kicks in pretty fast. But, I say Eric is a strong swimmer. He drowned because when he hit the water, he momentarily panicked, sucked in water, couldn't catch his breath, and that's what drowned him before he could reach the shore.

"The guys at the police department told me all the rest. They found the canoe first – the next morning washed up on Shimmo just east of the harbor, the paddle floating alongside it. Eric was not so fast, and he probably bloated up for a couple of days before he rose up to the surface where the currents floated him on over to Shimmo just like the canoe."

Gerry stopped talking abruptly as I struggled for something to say. "I'm sorry, Gerry. Eric was a good guy and I feel lucky to have known him. I know how close you two were; it must hurt a lot."

Gerry lifted his glass of beer again and chugged it on down. He looked at me hard, "Well, it's over for me too. Now that Eric's gone, I've decided that I've been in the Coast Guard too long. Maybe I'll pilot one shipment of dope up the inland waterway like those crazy Florida drug goons keep asking me to do. One time. Retire. And then I'll be sitting pretty."

"I think you would regret that Gerry." I said slowly.

"Hell no! I don't have any issues with that Norton. I've paid my dues and then some. The Coast Guard sure ain't gonna take care of me. Besides I bet Eric would really crack up at the idea after we have intercepted all these smugglers over the years. Shit, what a way to go out. Maybe I'll do it."

I waited while Gerry signaled the waiter to bring him another beer.

I wondered if it was the booze and the grief talking or if Gerry was actually talking himself into this act of rage, for that is how I would describe it.

I could see that everything had changed for him in the instant that Eric had fallen out of that canoe.

"Yeah, I've paid my dues," he said again. "Eric and I have been the best goddamn coxswains at the Brant Post Coast Guard for over 150 years and all I ever got was a stupid little commendation of appreciation from the Nantucket Yacht Club. I mean, is that it?"

As I left Gerry that night I hoped it was all in jest but I worried about him all the next day. He did not return to the Tavern the next night, as he had almost every night in the off-season. A few days later when I did not see him around I went by the Brant Point Station to check on him; to see if he was alright.

They told me Gerry had taken 30 days of emergency leave. He had mentioned something about an illness in the family. But Chief Petty Officer Joe Styles, who had been a friend of Gerry's was troubled.

"We all thought it was kinda strange. He almost never took off time in his years of service. He had accumulated three months of leave if he wanted it. Anyways he got two weeks of emergency leave approved two days ago. Then he just split two days ago without saying diddly to anyone. I knew he was shook up about Eric and he was acting real strange. I was sitting on a bench outside the station house and I saw him across the street at a phone booth making a call. It lasted about thirty minutes. I know that because I just sat there, watching him. Then he walks right past me not saying a word, goes to his room and comes out with his duffel bag. I thought maybe it was his family telling him to get home quick. That's why I figured he didn't take time to tell me about it."

"Not bloody likely" I thought, as I thanked Joe Styles and walked away.

I figured the only family Gerry had talked to in that phone call dealt in marijuana and cocaine. I was afraid that Gerry had made his pact with the devil to pilot one large drug shipment from somewhere in the Keys on up to a destination on the inland waterway for immediate pickup. I knew Gerry had the expertise to pilot a drug boat without getting caught by the Coast Guard as he had always played the game from the other side. Who better to beat the Coast Guard than someone from his background?

"One good run," he had said. A payoff of 100k. He would use the money to buy a fishing boat, sock some away and use the rest to send to Eric's ex-wife and child. All this he had said to me at the Tavern just a few weeks before. I had hoped it had all been an angry rant to be discarded by the next day. Now I was really afraid for Gerry.

But what if Gerry could do "just one run" and retire from the drug trade? Would his new family let such a valuable commodity leave the family? Maybe it would all turn out alright. But I doubted it. The Nantucket water had reclaimed Eric and that was probably where he wanted to be, just not that soon…. and not that way.

Gerry never came back to Nantucket Island or the Brant Point Station. After 60 days he was declared absent without leave (AWOL). After about 90 days he was found in the surf somewhere on the Florida Keys. He had washed up on a reef with a bullet in his head.

The Nantucket winter waterman blues had gotten them both.

And I was left to tell their story.

## THE CHASE

### *Chapter 1*

It had all begun on a hot summer night.

"Norton, you'd better get that worthless piece of shit, bucket of bolts, off the road by the time the summer people go," Sgt. Dicker had said. "There's too much going on now, but when the population drops from 50,000 to about 7,000 in a couple of months, I can guarantee you I will personally take you off the road and impound your car. And believe me, it will cost you more to get it back than it's worth."

I had moved from my apartment on Polpis Road because Mr. Reed, owner of the Chicken Box, had asked me to caretake some houses he was building out Tom Nevers Way. There had been some vandalism and he thought my presence could prevent that, and he had asked me to live in one of the completed units. I agreed to do so.

Back to P.T. Dicker and the Chicken Box. As you know, the Chicken Box was the home of my favorite bar and current employer. It is also where

Sargent Dicker had developed a permanent dislike for me on that late summer night.

As many of you will recall, the Box was a delightfully dilapidated night club and pool hall. It was a favorite of the "Locals." Sgt. Dicker was off duty on that particular night but his mouth was not … especially after a couple of Long Island ice teas … and there I was, an unemployed waiter/writer practicing my various pool shots. Sgt. Dicker walked up and challenged me to a friendly game of nine-ball. By definition nine-ball is a betting game and is never friendly, but in my misplaced enthusiasm I accepted his challenge. We agreed on a "no call" rotation in which you hit the next ball in ascending order, and whatever happens after that, whatever balls drop in a pocket, stay down. The two money balls in our game were the five and the nine. This variation on the nine-ball game was lightening quick, one in which you could make or lose a lot of money quickly.

We established five dollars on the five ball and ten dollars on the nine. Dicker won the roll for break. With an audible crash, he slammed the cue ball into the triangular rack, hitting the nine-ball into the three-ball which dropped into the side pocket. Dicker proceeded to shoot, with some precision, balls one, two, and four before he then missed a tricky bank shot on the five-ball which was, of course, the first money ball. Dicker smirked as we both saw that the five-ball was hidden by the seven-ball, making it almost impossible to get to it without a double bank. He missed the connection and handed off the cue stick to me. There was only one stick per table … well it was the Chicken Box. "I know you can't touch that five, Norton," roared Dicker in laughter. "But, hell, if you can actually kiss the nine-ball off the five, I'll pay you double."

Since I had nothing to lose on this nearly impossible shot, I tried to visualize the difficult path the cue ball would have to take, a double bank if I was to have a chance to hit the five-ball. I had no idea what would happen after that.

I lined up my shot, took a deep breath, and let it go.

Unbelievably, the cue ball did its necessary double bank, and hit the five-ball cleanly, which dropped into the side pocket. Then, even more unbelievably, it rolled down towards the end pocket and kissed the nine-ball safely into it.

Sgt. Dicker, his shirt tails hanging down over a sizable paunch, and chomping on an unlit cigar, was momentarily speechless. Then he spoke.

"You lucky little prick. Okay, you win the first round. That's $30 to you on the double or nothing bet. Now, set 'em up again. I'm gonna clean your clock."

"That's what you said before, Dicker," said Fred Coffin, another off-duty cop who had been watching and was now laughing hysterically.

"I can't wait to tell the boys about this."

"Oh, shut up, Fred. Just watch me take this little creep to school. I knew when to take a bow and leave the stage."

But I, Joe Norton, demurred.

"No, thanks, Sgt. Dicker. No rubber game for me," I said. "You're right. You would probably beat me. I'll just take my winnings and go home, thank you."

"Why you little punk," growled Dicker, as he took a couple of steps towards me. This made me nervous. Dicker was 6'3" and about 240 lbs. He had the reputation for being one very tough character.

"Go ahead and pay him, Dicker," warned Fred Coffin. "He won the money fair and square. We all saw it … a truly amazing shot … and we're not going to forget it. A pool hall story like this will last straight through the winter. And guess what, Dicker, you're gonna be the chump," Fred chuckled.

Dicker looked around atthe gathering crowd. They waited to see what he would do. He glared first at Coffin and then at me. He threw a wadded up twenty and ten-dollar bill at me. "You take that money and get out of here, Norton … but I can promise you I will find a way to make you regret not giving me a chance to win my money back. You'd better watch your back."

I smiled and waved at the Chicken Box crowd as I eased on out of there. It had been a great win, the kind legends are made from, however undeserved. I cherished that moment of my lucky shot, though I did wonder what cost Dicker would try to exact from me somewhere down the road. Still, it had been a good night, and maybe Sgt. Dicker would forget all about it in the coming days.

Unfortunately, as I heard more than once, his buddies in uniform *wouldn't* let him forget it. One had even drawn a large caricature of me hunkered down over a pool table making this incredible combo shot on the five- and the nine-ball. I looked pretty cool, while a grizzled overweight Dicker with shirttail hanging out was watching in disbelief. The drawing made the rounds and Dicker got a lot of ribbing.

In this much smaller Nantucket fall community, everybody seemed to know what everyone else was doing. The word was that Dicker was gunning for me and I needed to lay low. But as I said before, Nantucket is a small island, and smaller still when the summer dwellers leave. I still needed to get around, but I knew that if Dicker ever saw me in my battered old Chevy station wagon, he would hit me with every vehicle violation known to man.

*Chapter 2*

So, there I was in late November, a couple of months after the Chicken Box pool encounter. It was a glorious sky-blue day and it was cold. I was driving my 1968 V-8 Chevy station wagon. It was full of rust with holes in the floor board which I had covered with a stray stop sign. It had a cracked windshield, a blown-out rear window, and you could always hear the dulcet tones from the rusted muffler beneath her. But she did have a tough engine, which copious amounts of oil had sustained indefinitely. Mystery, my long-haired black cocker dachshund mongrel, and my partner in everything, was taking a brief nap in the back seat. It was going to be a good day.

I knew I had to watch out for Sgt. Dicker, but what were the odds he would see us at dawn way out here away from town? We were on the Madaket Road headed towards Hither Creek where we often took an early morning walk.

The stop sign shifted below me as I saw a police car coming from the opposite direction. I scrunched down in my seat as we passed each other and snuck a look over to the squad car. It was Dicker and he had "made" me or at least "made" the car. "Well, of course he had made me, you idiot," I told myself. "How many other cars looked like mine?"

I looked in my rearview mirror to see Dicker's squad car brake lights come on and I could hear his siren. I could also hear the squeal of tires as he executed a violent 180 degree turn on the narrow Madaket Road. I was in for it now. Instinctively, I gunned my car as blue smoke flew out of the exhaust. I knew

I had about 30 seconds, maybe fewer, before Dicker would descend upon me and issue a ticket for multiple violations. He would probably impound my car as well. I found myself speeding away to the sound of Dicker's siren in the distance. I realized that in addition to all my vehicle violations, I could now be charged with failure to stop for a police officer. That could be a felony.

At first I thought I should just pull over. Dicker was bound to catch me. Then, immediately in front of me and on the left, I saw the entrance to the Nantucket Dump, famous for garbage and seagulls, and providing some of the best secondhand furniture that my family's cottage had ever seen.

Since I had shopped many times at the Dump, I knew the terrain pretty well. I also knew the dump master, whom I found seated on his giant earthmoving bulldozer. I skidded left onto the dump road and eased up beside him. I hoped Dicker, coming over the horizon, hadn't seen me slide off the road into the dump. There was old O.K. Sanders, sitting idly on his big dozer.

I pulled up and told him about my predicament. "Can you help me?" I asked, telling him that Dicker was after me.

"Oh, yeah, I loved that pool hall story," he grinned. "People are still talking about it. I guess it's because we all hate that asshole Dicker. He's the meanest son of a bitch on the Island. Hey, maybe he's impacted. Huh!" O.K. laughed at his own joke. Then as he saw Dicker in his squad card entering the dump road, he spoke quickly.

"Park that wreck over there behind that mound of garbage I just plowed up. Stay down and be quiet. I'll come for you when it's clear."

I parked under the protection of the sand dunes and one giant mound of moldering garbage where hundreds of fatted gulls were dining out. They were holding a raucous cacophony of bird talk, and I could barely hear O.K. Sanders talking with Sgt. Dicker.

Meanwhile, Mystery, my first mate, was being uncharacteristically quiet in the face of this sea of menacing seagulls. I could just barely hear Dicker's voice not too far away. He sounded even angrier than usual, "Did you see that little bastard from Virginia drive in here? He's driving a light blue 1968 rusting Chevy station wagon. I know he went off the main road somewhere around here."

"Why, no, Dicker, I didn't," said O.K. "Why do you want to see him … you wanna set up another nine-ball game?"

"Very funny, Sanders. No, I want him for about 25 vehicle violations and now for failure to stop for a police officer. That little prick is gonna practice nine-ball behind bars when I get through him. Now, is he here or not?"

There was a brief silence from O.K. Sanders. Then, "Do you see him here, Dicker? I gotta go back to work. You wanna look for him over there in the garbage mounds, be my guest."

Sanders started up his giant bulldozer. There was almost too much noise for me to hear, but since Dicker was practically yelling at O.K., I could still make it out.

"Well, I promise you this, Sanders, and anyone else who knows Norton. Tell him he's dead meat. I've just radioed for backup what with Norton now being a fugitive from justice and all. You and I both know there's not much going on this time of year, so we're just gonna comb this island until we find him." After he left, there was silence as the bulldozer engine suddenly stopped. O. K. Sanders appeared on foot around the giant garbage mound. He walked quickly up to my car.

"You're in a world of hurt now, Norton. You can't put that car back on the road … ever! They'll get you for sure. Dicker has blood in his eye … and you can't leave that car here because Dicker would fry my ass for hiding you. So, here's what you do. You see that dirt road over there at the end of the dump? It will take you south in the direction of Cisco Beach. As you get close, you'll see more trails headed east above the shore towards S'conset town. You live out Tom Nevers way now, right?" I nodded. "Well, if you get back there to your place just leave it in the woods or scrub pine. Don't ever try to move it again. If you don't get there, abandon your car wherever it gets stuck and remember, you can never drive that car on this island again. Now, get going … I never saw you. Remember that, too."

O.K. Sanders turned and walked back to his dozer, climbed up on his seat and brought the engine to a roaring start. Slowly, I emerged from behind the garbage mound and inched my old car past Sanders, saluting him as I did so. He tipped his old Nantucket Whalers cap. I proceeded down a narrow dirt road in the general direction of Cisco Beach … away from Sgt. Dicker and Madaket Road.

Mystery and I drove through the brush and thickets of Nantucket Moor on a sandy road towards Cisco Beach. Mystery placed her front paws on the passenger arm rest as she stuck her head out the window to better observe the passing jungle.

I thought we would get stuck at any moment, but it had been uncharacteristically dry the previous two months. The sand and dirt were packed hard on the surface, and we were able to continue to plod along. Just as I approached the sand dunes overlooking the beach, I spotted what appeared to be an old Indian trail near the shoreline, headed towards my cottage at Tom Nevers Way some six miles away.

It didn't really matter whether the car made it all the way or not, it was only necessary to get far enough away from the dump and Sgt. Dicker in order that I could build a foundation of "deniability" with regard to where I was when he thought he had spotted me in my car.

Amazingly, one road led to another trail east, and each time there was a fallen log or other obstruction. I was able to get around it and keep going … all the way to the Coast Guard Road which led to Tom Nevers Way and onto the cottage where I lived.

I parked the old Chevy far back in the woods behind the house, took off the license plate and left it to die, never to see the road again. I calculated it would take about 20 years to rust away right down to the chassis. Of course, it already had a pretty good start.

Now, how to counter the "failure to stop" warrant, I was sure Dicker would swear out against me? Let's see — he never actually saw me before he did his "180" as I had scrunched down to keep my head below the glass of my door. I also don't believe he ever actually saw my car turn into the dump. In addition, O.K. Sanders never acknowledged that I had been there.

I don't like to lie — but sometimes in the interest of the greater good, namely mine and that of Mystery, and if asked by the court, I might have to deny that I was in the vicinity of the dump off Mataket Road at the same time Dicker would say he had seen me there. It was a matter of survival. What I would say was that my car had been parked behind my cottage where I had been working on my short stories inside the house all day long. This scenario seemed plausible to me as it was known on the Island that I was working on a book and often talked about it.

For the rest of that day, I actually *did* do some writing. It was a short story about a recent suicide by drowning in the Nantucket harbor. I took a break only to walk Mystery down to Pebble Beach and breathe in the ocean air. When we returned to the cottage, I continued to work on that same short story all afternoon. If Dicker were coming to get me, he knew where I lived. Why was he taking so long to get there? Well, maybe he got distracted by another case. Maybe I had gotten lucky.

It was right about then that I heard the siren of an approaching car. I came out and stood on the porch and watched as it roared up my driveway. 'Good old' Sgt. Dicker leapt out of the car and came running in my direction. A second officer I recognized as Charlie Stackpole followed along behind. (Nantucket is a small community and with a police department composed of about 22 men, it was easy to recognize most of them if you lived here long enough.) Dicker grabbed me by both shoulders and shoved me against the front door. He told me to turn around. I did so. He slapped handcuffs tight on my wrists.

Officer Stackpole eased his way up from behind and said, "Hey, Dicker, you don't have to cuff him. Jeeezzz, let's just take him into town and have him arraigned. He's harmless enough."

"Shut up, Charlie," said Sgt. Dicker to the other cop. "I've got this little son of a bitch. If it hadn't been for the paperwork, I'd have gotten here sooner." Dicker marched me down to his cruiser and opened the rear door. He pushed my head down and shoved me into the back seat. By now the cuffs were chafing my wrists. Dicker continued to talk as much for Stackpole's edification as mine. "This creep is being arrested for failure to stop for a police officer. That'll probably be a felony." Dicker told Officer Stackpole to stay with me while he looked in the back of the cottage for my old Chevy. He returned with a smile on his face.

"Yup, Norton, I found your car back there and I confirmed all the vehicle violations you were driving with on a public road this morning."

Dicker sat down in the front seat and leaned in my direction and said, "Norton, I'm guessing you figured you could drive down to the beach and just find your way home on those old Indian trails ... and then what? Just hide out from old Sgt. Dicker? You're a real smart ass, aren't you? But look who's going to jail."

I could hear Mystery barking furiously at the car as we pulled away.

Dicker continued to talk glowingly of my immediate future as we drove back to Nantucket Center. He was really enjoying himself.

"Hey, Dicker," Charlie Stackpole started.

"Quiet, Charlie! Can't you see I'm in the middle of painting a beautiful picture for Norton."

"But Dicker ...," Stackpole began.

"I said 'be quiet', bellowed Dicker. "Oh, all right. Spit it out. What is it, Charlie?"

"Well, you figure Norton drove that car here on all those back roads to avoid you?"

"Yeah, yeah, so what's your point?"

"Well, what if he claims he was home the whole time? That makes it his word against yours. Did you actually see him in the car as you passed it on Madaket Road?"

"Well, no, he had scrunched down in the driver's seat so I couldn't see him, but I sure as hell saw that rusty old car, you couldn't mistake it, and I saw his mutt looking out the back window, so that ought to be enough for a positive I.D."

Then he nodded to me and said, "Next stop Nantucket jail for you, Norton. And guess what? It's 5:30 on a Friday afternoon. That means no bail bondsman for you until Monday morning. As you know, Nantucket bail bondsmen take their weekends off very seriously."

We arrived at the station house. Dicker pulled me out of the car and walked me inside. I was frisked, my handcuffs removed, and directed towards a rather dank holding cell. The bars closed behind me as Dicker gave me a parting shot. "You get one call, Norton. Better make it count. There is no weekend bail bondsman, so even if you called a lawyer he can't get you out until you've been arraigned on Monday morning. Enjoy your weekend. By the way, you'll probably be heard by Judge Eddins, and he hates smart asses almost as much as I do."

Sgt. Dicker continued. "Well, I hope you enjoy your weekend accommodations. Hey, maybe you can practice nine-ball of the mind. Heh, heh."

So, a three-day all expenses paid vacation in the Nantucket Center Jail became my immediate future. I only hoped that Mystery would be all right. There was food and water in the house and long ago I had rigged an escape hatch so that she could get in and out whenever she wanted.

But she would miss me.

*Chapter 3*

The following Monday after enjoying all the luxuries the Nantucket Center Jail could afford, I met bail which was set at $200. I had to write a check for that amount. Normally only a cash bond would be acceptable, but, as I said, Nantucket is a small town in the off-season and I knew the bail bondsmen. I had waited on him on several occasions at the Whale Restaurant so he was indulgent.

"Norton, I'm taking your check. If it does not clear at the Pacific Bank, we will come and get you."

"Thanks," I said, smiling at him. "I just deposited $250 worth of tips from your favorite restaurant."

"Alright," he said. "I understand you'll be arraigned and the hearing held promptly tomorrow. There isn't much of a workload since the summer dwellers left. Court starts at nine o'clock, so let me give you a little advice. Make sure you're there early. Judge Eddins starts promptly, and if you're even a minute late he won't be happy. You don't want that."

"Got it," I said.

I escaped to the outside, where I spotted Eddie Robbins in his one-car taxi company. "Eddie, can you take me to Tom Nevers? I've been in jail for three days, thanks to Sgt. Dicker, and I've got to get home to take care of my dog."

"Sure, hop in Norton," said Eddie. "Let's see. It's six miles to Tom Nevers Way. I'm not doing anything so I'll comp you this ride. Get in."

On the way I told Eddie, in confidence, the whole truth about the chase and being put in handcuffs and taken to jail.

"The son of a bitch," said Eddie. "You've got to tell them you weren't there. Dicker can't prove it and it's your word against his. By the way, you say Judge Eddins is presiding. Word is he doesn't like Dicker's attitude any more than I do, so that should help you. As far as I'm concerned, you never talked to me about any of this and I don't know anything about it."

I thanked Eddie as he dropped me off at my cottage. He left me with a parting gift: "Okay, Norton, you've got to be in court by 9:00 tomorrow morning. I'll be here at 8:15 to take you in. No charge, you not having a working car any more. After that, you and your dog are on your own. How's that sound?"

"Great," I said, reaching in the driver's side window to shake his hand. "It's nice you want to help me out," I said.

"Hey, Norton, we Islanders help anyone crazy enough to spend fall and winter here. We like that. It almost makes you one of us. Almost." Eddie smiled and backed out of the driveway. He waved as he headed back to Nantucket Center.

I rushed in to Mystery, who had been barking furiously ever since she heard my voice outside.

She stood in a far corner as I entered the cottage. For a moment, she just stared at me. It was her way of telling me she was extremely annoyed at my leaving her alone for three days, and more importantly, that I had not taken her with me in the first place.

"Come on, girl," I said. "I really couldn't help it. Come here, girl." I dropped to my knees and motioned to her with a smile. "Please." She could resist no longer. With two loud barks she rushed over and threw herself into my arms, all 30 pounds of her, and began licking my face furiously. I had been forgiven as only a best friend would do.

I fed Mystery a bowl of kibble, and bologna I had cut into little pieces. I had a beer and a bologna sandwich myself. After lunch, we walked down to the ocean, a half mile from the cottage. It was cold and the wind was blowing but the sun was shining. It was clear and bright. As we walked along, Mystery barked at imaginary enemies while looking back at me to make sure I was still with her. It was a glorious walk and, since the area was largely uninhabited, Mystery could run free. She barked and ran from left to right, creating a kind of joyous zig zag only to come back to brush against my trousers. I was home base and she didn't want me to disappear again.

Once we got there, Mystery chased wave after wave, barking at them and then escaping from them as they rushed back in upon her. Suddenly, a "rogue wave" caught her unexpectantly and bowled her over with its near freezing salt water. She quickly swam out of it and rushed for shore where she shook herself off. She was miserable and wet … and probably upset that the wave had beaten her at her own game.

"Come on, girl," I said. "Let's get you home and dried off. Once we get there, I'll plan my strategy for Judge Eddins tomorrow." It was as if I was having a conversation with her. Well, on some level I believe she did understand – better than some people. "I've got to go in tomorrow and you might be an orphan again for a short time." Mystery gave me a look of deep concern as if she knew what I was saying.

"Oh, don't worry," I said. "I'll get Alice from the 'Whale' to take care of you. She got to know you pretty well when I used to bring you to that restaurant on my work days. I will call her. I'm sure she will take care of you if something happens to me temporarily."

Mystery was looking at me intently. Maybe she did understand.

"Don't worry, Mystery. I'm going to beat these charges and everything will be just fine for you and me." Mystery trotted over and pressed herself hard against me. She scratched insistently at my trousers. I picked her up and gave her a kiss right on the snout. She looked a little indignant, but not entirely. She began licking me on the face.

"Alright, alright," I said laughing, as I put her down. "Let's have a little decorum around here." But Mystery was having none of it. She began to growl as she bit my trouser leg playfully. Her tail was wagging furiously. I knelt down and gently pushed her away. I was smiling and she was smiling as she rushed back and leapt into my arms.

It was going to be all right.

### *Chapter 4*

I arrived at court on Tuesday at 8:45    thanks to Eddie. I saw a lot of people I knew. Mostly they were there to contest various speeding violations and there was one for reckless driving. The names and violations were listed on the door as I walked in.

The speeding tickets, Judge Eddins dispatched in the usual way, dropping the speeding violations five to ten miles an hour when he received a plea of guilty, and exacting the full amount if the defendant pleaded not guilty on the usual claim of "I don't think I was going that fast" or the like.

As to the reckless driving case, the violation was driving 66 miles per hour in a 45 mile per hour zone. The defendant seemed terrified. His face was perspiring and sweat darkened his shirt at the armpits.

When the Judge asked if he had any defense, the man explained his dog had been hit by a car and badly hurt. He was speeding to the vet because he thought his dog might die of blood loss before he got there. "I have a witness," he said.

"Well, let's bring him up here Mr., err, Lilly and hear what he has to say."

The witness, Dr. Barry Brown, was smiling as he strode up to the bench.

"Well, as I live and breathe, it's my old friend, Dr. Brown. How've you been?" asked Judge Eddins.

"Just fine, Judge."

"Looks like you've put on a little weight, Barry," said the Judge. "Must have been that good cookin' of the Missus."

They both laughed. Then Judge Eddins looked over hard in the direction of Sgt. Dicker, who was seated near the front of the courtroom. He was waiting to be called up for this case.

"Sgt. Dicker — Dr. Brown is a friend of mine — been lookin' after my Golden Retrievers for years — now that's not going to affect how I handle this hearing. Is that going to be a problem for you? You think you might need another judge? Would you like me to recuse myself?"

There was silence. "Well? Speak up Dicker," said the judge ominously.

"Err, no problem," said Dicker, looking down at his feet.

"Good, now I bet we'll get this resolved pretty quickly," said the judge. "Alright, Dicker, tell the court what happened."

"Pretty simple," said Dicker. "I clocked the defendant going 66 miles an hour up S'conset Road in a 45 mile per hour zone. I pulled him over and issued the ticket."

The judge interrupted Dicker. "So that's 66 in a 45 mile per hour zone, that is 21 miles per hour over the speed limit and that makes the driving charge 'reckless' by one mile per hour. Is that right, Dicker?"

"Well, yes, sir, that's what he was doing," said Dicker.

"Mr. Lilly says his dog was in the back of the car. Is that right?"

"Yes, sir."

"What condition was he in?" asked the judge.

"Well, I don't know. He was bleeding a little, but not bad, I didn't think."

"Okay," interrupted Judge Eddins. "You can sit down, Sgt. Dicker."

The judge turned to the vet and said, "Now, Barry, uh Dr. Brown, in your expert opinion what condition was the dog in when the defendant got him to your office."

"Well, Judge, he had lost a lot of blood. There was internal bleeding as well."

"Would you say this was an emergency?" asked the judge.

"Absolutely — old Charlie - that's the name of Mr. Lilly's collie dog - I've treated him for years and I believe he was pretty close to death. He probably would have died if he'd gotten to me much later, from loss of blood."

Sgt. Dicker stood up abruptly. "I don't think he needed to drive that fast. If Lilly had driven 45 miles an hour instead of 66 miles an hour, he would have gotten there almost as quick, maybe three or four minutes later."

"Sit down, Sgt. Dicker," bellowed the judge. "You are out of order. One more outburst and I will put you in contempt of court. Do you understand me?"

Dicker nodded his head, slowly.

"Then sit down and be quiet until, and unless, I call you up again. You got that?"

"Yes, sir," said Dicker. He sat down slowly and glared at the judge as if he were angry with him.

Probably not a good look.

"Okay, the Court has heard the witness and heard the defendant and heard Sgt. Dicker," said the judge. "It is my considered opinion that the defendant drove at an excessive rate of speed. Still, he believed he was doing it to save the life of his dog. Sgt. Dicker didn't think so. Dr. Brown did. I'm going with the expert opinion over yours, Dicker. I'm going to suspend this case for six months. I'm going to nolle pros it, and, if in that time Mr. Lilly acquires no more speeding violations, I will dismiss this case and it will be as if it never happened. But don't get any more moving violations in the meantime, Mr. Lilly, or you'll be in very hot water. Do you understand me, Mr. Lilly?"

Yes, sir, and thank you."

"Don't thank me. I did what I thought was right. Now, how is Old Charlie, the collie?"

"He's had a hard time, Judge, but I think he's gonna make a full recovery. He's a great dog."

"Well, I just bet he is," said Judge Eddins. "Say hello to Charlie for me, will you?"

The whole court laughed in full support of Mr. Lilly and Charlie ... everyone except Sgt. Dicker.

Judge Eddins smiled. "That's fine. Alright, next case."

"Yes, Sir," said the Clerk of Court. "Mr. Joe Norton is accused of failure to stop for a police officer, faulty headlights, blown out muffler, busted out rear window, unsafe and rusted out floor board, and four bald tires."

"Good Lord, who wrote this ticket up?"

"That's my ticket," said Sgt. Dicker.

"Oh, God, give me strength," said Judge Eddins, almost under his breath. "Well, why don't you and Mr. Norton come on up here and we'll see what's going on."

I walked up to face the judge, deciding not to even look in Dicker's direction. Nothing good could come of that.

"Well, Mr. Norton," said the judge, leaning forward with his hands extended out of his black robe. He shook them as if preparing for the vagaries of this case and intertwined them tightly. "Mr. Norton, that must be quite a car you have. Still running?"

"No, sir," I said. "It's rusting away in the woods behind the cottage where I live. I don't think I can even start it anymore."

"Hmm. Well, that sounds like a good thing," said the judge.

So far so good.

"According to this," said the judge, looking at a court document, "you live out Tom Nevers Way. How will you get around now?"

"I'll ride my bike or walk, sometimes I may get a ride or even take a cab when I can afford it."

"Hmm, that all sounds very invigorating. Good exercise, I suppose."

"Okay, let's get on with the case. Sgt. Dicker, I've already heard the charges. Why don't you enlighten me as to what actually happened?"

"Yes, Your Honor," said Dicker. "Well, I was driving to town on Madaket Road when I see this guy coming by in the opposite direction in his bucket of bolts."

"You mean, Mr. Norton."

"Err, yes, sir. I know this guy and his car … and his dog. I've seen him around. And I told him to keep this car off the road. Anyway, when I saw him coming by me the other way towards Madaket …"

Judge Eddins interrupted. "Did you actually see Mr. Norton in the car?"

"Well, no, not exactly your honor. I think he had scrunched down in the front seat as he went by so I couldn't actually see him. But of course I did recognize the car and I did see his dog staring out at me from the busted rear window so I knew it was him."

"Okay, then what?"

"Well, I turned around as quick as I could, but by the time I got my speed up he had disappeared, down the dump road, I think."

"How do you know that?"

"'Cuz it was the only road off Madaket Road right there. He couldn't have turned off anywhere else."

"I see," said the Judge, mildly. "Well, go on."

"Well, then I saw old O.K. Sanders, the dump master sittin' on his big bulldozer so I asked him where Norton was."

"Okay, what did he say?" Judge Eddins wanted to know.

"He said I could look anywhere I wanted, but he didn't say whether Norton had been there or not."

"Interesting."

"Yes, Sir, well I believe he was covering for Norton because they are friends, and O.K. and I don't get along so good. So, I think he was covering up just to give me a hard time."

"And how do you know that O.K. and Norton are friends?"

"Because I know that Norton gets all his furniture out there at the dump. You know, those summer dwellers dump their old furniture out here so they can redecorate their houses or mansions or something. I know Norton hangs out there a lot so that he can pick up some of this 'gently used furniture' to outfit his cottage. When I take my garbage to the dump, I often see Norton talking to Sanders. So, like I say, I know they must be friends. And you know what, Judge? I think Sanders was lying to me about not seeing Norton."

"Do you have any proof of that, Sgt. Dicker?"

"Well, no, Judge, but he had to be lying. How else could Norton just turn off on the dump road, go into the dump, and disappear into thin air without Sanders seeing him?"

Judge Eddins sighed audibly. "Okay, Dicker, tell me what happened then. I want to wrap this up so I can go to lunch. Pick up your pace, if you don't mind."

"Yes, sir, Your Honor," said Dicker quickly. "I think what Norton did was drive that car out the dirt road at the end of the dump and head south down towards Cisco Beach. There he probably picked up one of those old Indian trails and headed east and somehow got that vehicle back to Tom Nevers Way and on down to his cottage. Later that day I went down to pick him up for refusal to stop for a police officer. I had the warrant with me, Judge. I found the car out behind his cottage sort of hidden in the trees and brush. That's where I confirmed all the vehicle violations I assumed he was driving with on the Madaket Road. So, I proceeded to write up a ticket for all those violations in addition to the failure to stop for an officer."

"Okay Dicker, go back to how this all started. When did you first see him and what was he doing?"

"Oh, yes, Your Honor. Like I said, I was headed east to town from my house. I spotted Norton as he passed me headed in the opposite direction towards Madaket. Since I knew then that his car shouldn't even be on the road, I did a 180 to pull him over, but he had disappeared, I assumed down the Dump Road. It was the only road off the Madaket Road in that area. It's pretty obvious what he did after that. When Officer Stackpole and I caught up with him at his cottage, that's when I confirmed the violations on his car as well."

"So, that's what you did, eh," said the judge in a measured tone. "Okay, hang on right there. Let's see what Mr. Norton has to say." He turned to me, "Okay, Mr. Norton, what is your version of this great escape? Please don't take too long – no pressure, but my lunch hour's coming up and I don't want to miss it. I'm hungry so stick to the facts, please. Spare me the long version. Okay, go."

No pressure! Wow. I knew I'd better be succinct and I'd better be quick. "Well, Your Honor, this whole thing has been a mystery to me. I was at my cottage off Tom Nevers Way working on a short story virtually that whole day. Suddenly, I heard a siren and I went out on the porch to see what was going on. A police car had pulled up in my driveway and Sgt. Dicker jumped out. He ran up to me saying something about having a warrant for my failure to stop for a police officer. He threw me up against my front door, cuffed me, and led me down to his car where he held my head down and pushed me into the back seat. Sgt. Dicker then took me into Nantucket Center to the town jail where he advised me that I would have to stay for the weekend, this being Friday afternoon, because he was sure the bail bondsmen had gone home for the weekend and wouldn't be back until Monday morning.

"It was a long weekend, Your Honor, but I made bail on Monday and got home to take care of my dog. That was yesterday and here I am today for this hearing. That's pretty much it, Your Honor."

The judge looked at me intently. "Pretty much it, is it?" he said. He then looked over to Sgt. Dicker. "I guess lunch will just have to wait," said the judge. "I'm going to have to go into my chambers to review the testimony before I give my decision. You two can just sit down and wait. I'll be back in about twenty minutes or so. This is a tough one."

Judge Eddins got up as the clerk yelled, "All rise." The judge disappeared through the door to his chambers.

Twenty minutes can take forever. I kept looking at my watch as the minute hand seemed to move ever so slowly.

Finally, the judge emerged to render his decision. Again, the congregation rose and sat down as the judge settled into his chair.

"Alright, Mr. Norton, Sgt. Dicker. Come on up here and we'll get this over with."

As we stood before Judge Eddins, I looked over and saw that Sgt. Dicker was looking straight at me. He smiled at me with what could only be called "a confident sneer."

Judge Eddins began. "This is one of the most convoluted cases I've had the pleasure of presiding over in a long time. You each give a very different version of what happened, so I am going to stick to the actual facts as I now know them.

"Let's see. Sgt. Dicker, you say Mr. Norton was in the car you tried unsuccessfully to catch and pull over. You say Mr. Norton was in that vehicle but you never actually saw him clearly. You think you identified his dog looking out the rearview window but you can't be sure. You say O.K. Sanders wouldn't confirm whether Norton was at the dump or not, but you think he was lying. Oh, and you think Mr. Norton escaped from the dump, taking a dirt road south towards Cisco Beach, and then was able to successfully navigate various Indian trails east towards Tom Nevers Way and then onto his cottage. Well, that's quite an adventure right there."

Judge Eddins removed his glasses and wiped them very carefully with a small white cloth before putting them back on. Afterwards, he continued. "Okay, now as I understand your testimony, Sgt. Dicker, you arrested Norton at his house and put him in handcuffs and then shoved him into the back of your car with Officer Stackpole. I think that's when you said you went around back to identify his car and that's when you wrote up all those violations on a car you can't even prove had been on the highway that morning. Then you took Mr. Norton back to the city jail where he stayed for two days before he was allowed to post bond.

"Listen to me carefully, Sgt. Dicker. You never established beyond a reasonable doubt that Norton was even in the car you passed that morning in question. And, you can't prove the dog you saw peering out of the broken back window was his. You don't know if that car belonged to him. You certainly didn't prove that O.K. Sanders was lying about whether Norton was there. And finally, you haven't presented any evidence that Norton escaped from the Nantucket dump where he supposedly was hiding, and somehow got his car all the way back to his cottage off Tom Nevers Way."

Judge Eddins crossed his arms, leaned down towards Sgt. Dicker, and spoke quietly. "Basically, Sgt. Dicker, you have failed to prove any of the essential elements of this case." Then the judge spoke with considerable volume and deliberately. "You only presented conjecture."

He continued, "What I do know is that you arrested Mr. Norton at his home, possibly used excessive force while providing no justification for it. Mr. Norton may well have grounds against you for this unnecessary treatment." Judge Eddins turned to me and continued, "However, Mr. Norton. I wouldn't pursue this avenue if I were you. There are some circumstances about this case that you might not want examined any further.

"As I said, this case is full of circumstantial evidence which in part or in whole is unsubstantiated. There is no proof of almost anything that happened and so the charges you placed, Sgt. Dicker, may be true or not, but they certainly were never proven. Therefore, I am dismissing this case for lack of evidence … and I am now going to lunch." Judge Eddins stood up and once again the clerk called us all to rise. Judge Eddins disappeared into his chambers from which, I assume, he went off to a nice lunch.

Naturally, I couldn't have been happier with the findings of the judge and his subsequent dismissal of all charges. Meanwhile, Dicker looked stunned. He was certainly not happy about the dismissal of all charges. He glared at me before stomping down the aisle and out of the courtroom.

I waited a couple of minutes before I exited the courtroom. I wanted to give Dicker plenty of time to leave before I appeared. When I walked outside, I breathed a large sigh of relief as I spotted Eddie, who was waiting for me in his taxi. He laughed at the results of my hearing, even as he dropped me off at my cottage. I gave him a large tip and he was smiling as he drove off. I smiled too as I started to go in to tell Mystery all about it.

Suddenly, I saw Eddie turn around and drive back. He rolled down his window and said, "This result is great for you, but you better avoid Dicker for a while. This is the second time you've made a fool of him and you can't tell what he might do. He's going to stay angry at you for a long time." Then Eddie smiled again and drove off.

I rushed into the cottage to share my victory with Mystery. I would worry about Dicker later. I did believe Dicker would try to seek some sort of revenge at some point in the future, and that was worrying. But in my joy of the moment, and in the happiness Mystery was showing me, well, paraphrasing what Scarlet O'Hara said in *Gone with the Wind*, "I will think about that tomorrow."

## SEASON'S GREETINGS and
## SAYING GOODBYE TO ALL THAT

After the drowning of my friend Eric, and the disappearance of Gerry, both coxswains in the Nantucket's U.S. Coast Guard, I needed to get away. In early December, I took a one-week job working for a contractor who had been hired to do an emergency foam insulation job at a tavern in Keene, New Hampshire, of all places. He was a friend of Mr. Reed, my boss at the Chicken Box.

"Take the job, Norton," he said. "You'll make some good money and, yes, you can take Mystery dog. But you better take some long johns for both of you. There's some bitter weather up there this time of year."

There I was, two days later, blowing insulation into the guts of this old tavern. It was probably filled with asbestos already. It was five degrees and the wind was blowing. My jeans were frozen stiff as were my nose hairs, the air was sharp in my lungs as I inhaled. Meanwhile, I forced the foam through the holes in the white clapboard siding we had drilled earlier.

I looked through the window to the bar within and saw two men laughing and drinking "shots." One of them was my boss, who was supposed to be outside in the van mixing the next batch of foam insulation. And this was the third day in a row he had done this to me.

It was time to leave this job and go back to Nantucket.

I climbed down off the ladder and tapped on the window to get my boss's attention. I flipped him the bird as I mouthed a silent "fuck you!" I walked back to the motel, grabbed up Mystery, my dog, and my knapsack and walked towards the interstate entrance to begin hitchhiking home. It was just a few days before Christmas. Swell.

Unbelievably, after only about a fifteen-minute wait at the highway entrance, two girls from Boston College picked us up. I sat in the back seat feeling grateful. Then the cute brunette, whose name was Jeannie, looked at me through the rearview mirror and asked where I was going with that "cute little black dog."

"Nantucket," I said.

"Well, it's the holidays for us, and we are going to a party in Boston. Why don't you come along? We're all staying at my cousin's house. You two can crash with us and we will drive you on down to the ferry tomorrow."

I declined, saying I had to get straight back to Nantucket that night for work. I didn't, but that's how depressed I was.

They dropped us off at the exit for Hyannis and the steamship back to Nantucket. Jeannie actually looked sad about it all. She blew me a kiss as they drove off.

What an idiot I was for not accepting their holiday party weekend. It might have been fun, I thought. I'm such a dummy.

And that's how I felt when the Uncatena ferry pulled into the Nantucket harbor. Dumb and depressed. Other than my time with Mystery, I was not looking forward to much on this Christmas of 1978.

*Christmas Stroll*

A week or so before Santa came to Nantucket in 1978, there was something called the Christmas Stroll.

On this evening, there was always a high school marching band tripping its way down the Main Street cobblestones, and a myriad of holiday decorations… lots of Christmas joy.

The merchants threw open the doors to their stores and offered champagne and hors d'oeuvres. Musicians were playing up and down the street, fiddlers and guitar players. There were kids singing Christmas carols and the champagne really warmed our hearts. We were all year-rounders now and we were strong in our unity. Now that the summer dwellers and part-time people had left, it was just us here to celebrate our good fortune on this great occasion.

Of course, the very next day most of the merchants, who had celebrated with us the night before, had now boarded up their stores and headed south to Miami and Key West, all the warm places to push their wares. For them, the "Stroll" was merely a going away party while they left the "real" Nantucketers behind... and a little empty.

As for those of us left behind, we all felt a little deserted.

Time to get busy, the winter was here and we needed to plan for next year.

*Planning for Next Year*

So, what the hell were we real Nantucketers going to do now that the merchants had left, the Summer Dwellers had long since evaporated before them, and the Yacht Club members even before them. They had all left. But we had stayed. We were the real Nantucketers. Of course we celebrated our unity and toughness as we scrambled to figure out how we were going to get through the winter.

We now had a population that had receded from 50,000 in the summer to fewer than 5,000 at the end of December.

Unfortunately, those that had left had taken all their spending money with them.

Local places like the Chicken Box would get by. The people always needed a place to drink and eat and dance and commiserate about getting through Nantucket's winter. And the Box was their favorite year-round.

But what does a waiter do when most of the restaurants are closed until next summer, and what does the tradesman do when he has no work because most of his clients have gone back home to the mainland... and so on and so on.

For many Nantucket blue collar workers, there was the winter weekly unemployment check that kept them going, together with various odd jobs they could scrounge up.

And then there were the planning parties for next year.

With this vague concept in mind, I was quietly drinking with a couple of buddies at the Tavern Restaurant on a cold January evening. Yeah, hello to 1979. Some of our fellow islanders were going stir crazy – too much drinking, not enough work, too much time on their hands and the cold winter winds that were blowing across the island…and Santa had long ago taken his sleigh back to the North Pole.

But tonight, we were re-entering the dreamy world of brainstorming as we tried to figure out new ways to separate the summer dweller from more of his money in exchange for a Nantucket experience. After a couple of drinks, we like to think out of the box, to come up with a new angle to provide something that will dazzle and delight and encourage our annual visitors to buy something new and different... and more lucrative.

Out of the blue, my mind wandered back to when I was a mere toddler. The makers of Kellogg's Sugar Corn Pops had hit on a great new promotion. On the back of the cereal box we kids were offered a chance to own one square inch of Texas if we (or our parents) simply sent in a coupon together with a check for $3.99. In return we would own a piece of Texas, one square inch, and our purchase would even come with a written title to the property… even a vague location of where it might be.

Then it hit me. Why not buy 24 sq. feet of unusable land from Mr. Reed, my friend and boss at the Chicken Box (he would probably give it to me laughing at my chutzpah). I would break it into 144 square inches (per square foot) times twenty-four equals 3,456 square inches, each of which would sell for 9 dollars and 95 cents. The purchase price would include a deed and a map – you could actually go out to Tom Nevers Way and see your property.

There might even be a secondary market in which we would set up a kid with a lemonade stand who would sell that while our new owners were looking at their property.

Finally, the entire package would include a keychain which had a clear plastic dome over some sand grains, all to symbolize the Nantucket property you own.

My buddies agreed immediately that it was a hell of a deal. I mean if we sold out all 3,456 individual square inch properties at $9.95 each we would gross approximately $34,387.20! And there could be organized bus tours out to the new owners' property and maybe lunch and some lemonade to be bought on the bus. The sky was the limit.

We ordered another round at the Tavern to celebrate our glowing future. Tycoons in Nantucket square inch property sales. We were set. All we had to do was put the pieces together and it was going to be an absolute bonanza for all of us. We were gonna be rich.

More on this later. As a teaser I will tell you the deal did come together, but not quite in the way I had anticipated.

### The Call

The joys of Christmas had come and gone. It was a cold, wintry day in January of 1979. I found myself setting up for the evening at the Chicken Box and pretty much living day to day despite the good friends I had there, Mr. Reed and Sid and Robert.

When depression cycles came at me, I had learned how to delay their arrival. But, I couldn't prevent them. I would often medicate with alcohol but that only led to other problems.

Suddenly, I looked around. It was Robert holding up the phone.

"Somebody on the phone wants to get ahold of you, says he knows you. He's from New York City."

Nobody from my old days in New York City would have known where I was, I thought. I was curious, but suspicious as I picked up the phone.

"Hey, Norton, you old runaway. I've been trying to reach you all over. I finally called your parents in Virginia. They said that you were working at a place called the Chicken Box in Nantucket, Massachusetts. So here I am."

It was Clyde Simpson, a vice-president at Smyth Decline and Fault Advertising. Clyde was the boss of my old boss at my old advertising agency. When I left, he was already the number three guy in the agency. What would he want from me?

"You won't believe this," he said. "Your old client, Mainline Pharmacuticals in Philadelphia, wants you back, bad. They are still a $100-million dollar company and still have the number one product in the cold category.

Meanwhile, we have been making over fifteen million dollars a year in ad revenue from them. Everybody is happy except for your old brand manager and opposite number Joe Cranston. He is now vice-president of sales for the whole company. He said he always enjoyed working with you and he wants us to find you and get you back. Well, I am authorized to make you an offer right now. A great offer, but you have to come back to the Agency right away."

"Well, I don't know if I *am* interested at the moment," I said.

"Just wait a minute, Norton, and listen to what I am prepared to offer you. This is a multimillion-dollar account for us and we want to make sure the client is happy, and for some reason you have become the key to their happiness.

"So, here's the offer: we will double your previous salary, we will make you senior copywriter with full creative control over your accounts, and we will advance you five-thousand dollars to cover expenses… and you don't have to pay it back, Norton."

"Wow, you guys must be desperate," I said.

"We are. We want you to start by the end of next week."

"Come on, I don't even know where I would stay," I said.

"Yeah, we thought of that, too. You remember Bill Battle? He is still working on our American Express account and he has a lovely two-bedroom apartment midtown on the Eastside. We just sent him on international assignment to our offices in London. So, guess what? We will give you his apartment with six months of free rent while you look for another place of your own."

"Wow, that's some offer. Still, I have my dog Mystery with me. I'm not going anywhere without her."

"Damnit, Norton. It's a two-bedroom apartment! Mystery can have her own bedroom with a view of the park if that's what she wants."

"So, Norton, are you on board?" Clyde was almost shouting into the phone. He sounded a bit annoyed.

"Well, it's a really great offer. I just need some time to think it over."

"Okay Norton," said Clyde. "This is the best offer you are going to get in your life. The client was absolute that we get you back on his team. I do too but I have my limits. This is Thursday afternoon. You get back to me tomorrow, Friday by 3 p.m. That way I can get back to the client by five... and we will all have a good weekend. But, don't let me down Norton, don't let yourself down – don't let your dog down. Call me tomorrow by three or I promise you I will work it out another way... and you will be SOL. That's shit out of luck, Norton." He rang off.

## The Talk

I got off the phone, walked over to the bar and sat down. Before I could say anything, Mr. Reed looked down at me from across the bar. He was holding a glass up to the light, as if to wipe it clean, I thought. He then spoke.

"Norton, you look like you've seen a ghost. Bad news?"

"Well, not exactly. It might be good news. I just don't know if I'm ready for it."

"Okay, Norton," he said. "Give me the full picture. And don't hold back. I'm listening."

I summarized the rather incredible offer in detail for Mr. Reed. He listened intently before he responded.

"Norton, you've had your year on Nantucket and I think you needed it. You got some writing done, maybe you got your head on a little tighter, and you made some friends here. We will all be here for you when you come back. But this offer is one you won't get again. I think it provides a bridge to your future. You need to get back to the mainland, and this is your ticket."

Mr. Reed dropped his gnarly old face down so he was looking at me just inches away.

"I want you to take this offer Norton. I know you're a little bit nervous about it but you know that it is time for you to go back. You can finish working out your depression problems over there just as well as you can here. It's time.

"If you do not take this offer, I will fire you not only from here but also as caretaker of my housing development. Furthermore, I will have Robert, all 295 pounds of him, come find you and kick your ass!"

We both laughed, Mr. Reed said, "Now do it."

I said yes.

### Say Goodbye to All That

Three days after I had talked to Mr. Reed and two days after I had accepted the offer, I stood on the upper deck of the Uncatena looking down at all the people milling about. I guess these were all the people seeing their friends and family off on the ferry and back to the mainland.

Suddenly, I saw that craggy face sporting his usual tattered captain's hat standing next to Robert. They were looking up at me and smiling.

Mr. Reed yelled up and shook his fist. "It's a good thing I didn't have to send Robert after you." We laughed.

"We decided we were going to miss you a little, so we came to say goodbye. I guess we will miss Mystery more than you, she's a lot cuter."

I lifted Mystery up just above the railing so they could get one last glance at her.

"Oh, yeah, I love that dog," said Robert.

"Yeah, you too, Norton," said Mr. Reed. "Don't you forget us."

And I didn't. I remember those times with love and affection. I miss those people a lot... and I sure do miss Mystery.

### Own One Square Inch of Nantucket

When I left to go back to the ad world of New York, I donated all rights to my brilliant idea to the "planning group" which I left behind.

Unfortunately, and despite great initial enthusiasm, life and the Nantucket winter got in their way. A keychain with sand grains under a glass dome representing Nantucket was all that happened.

So, Nantucket entrepreneurs, the marketing genius of owning a piece of Nantucket still awaits you.

Consider this:

1.  You buy 24 of 96 or 200 square feet from some Nantucket landowner who has some fallow land he will sell you for peanuts.
2.  You create an actual deed for each square inch sold.
3.  Create a locater map with which a customer can view his own property.

4. You market the property by selling keychains with deeds enclosed and symbolic sand within the glass dome of the keyring.

Initially, this "Own a Piece of Nantucket" would be marketed by Nantucket retailers in exchange for their usual percentage – but a much larger secondary market can be built through the use of direct mail and other large audience tools.

Here's an example of how it would work, God willing.

| 24 sq feet yields | 3,456 sq. inches at $9.95 per sq. inch | = | $34,387.20 |
|---|---|---|---|
| 48 sq. feet yields | 6,912 sq. inches at $9.95 per sq. inch | = | $68,774.40 |
| 96 sq. feet yields | 13,824 sq. inches at $9.95 per sq. inch | – | $137,548.80 |
| 200 sq. feet yields | 28,800 sq. inches at $9.95 per sq. inch | = | $286,569.00 |

Hey guys. You don't need much "startup." A little sweat equity and your marketing genius will take you the rest of the way on marketing *"Own One Square Inch of Nantucket."* And anyway, it's another reason to go to Nantucket.

You're welcome.

**Other Stories**

## BILLY AND MISS JILL
### *A Catchapea Love Story*

Catchapea was an old mining town whose only symbol of its former prosperity was the once bustling Santa Fe Railroad Line from which once and future prospectors had long ago ceased coming, or had proceeded further down the line where "prospects were better." In fact, Catchapea had been left behind by progress, left to itself, and the town was okay with that.

The people loved the hard scrabble land they worked to grow their crops to feed their children… and to buy the seed and fertilizer to get next year's crop started. They were grateful for what they had and grateful for each other. But they did need a school teacher to teach their kids the three R's while the adults took care of their livestock and worked in the fields. They needed someone to help them. It was about that time when Miss Jill arrived.

Occasionally, and for no apparent reason, a passenger would debark specifically at the Catchapea station, not by mistake, but by design. It was usually a family member or someone on the run, or someone who wanted to find a place where they would just be left alone.

Such a person was Miss Jill, an itinerant school teacher who arrived on a hot, July morning and asked if there would be any work for her teaching the children. They said yes with alacrity.

The previous teacher had left months earlier with no notice, and the children were badly in need of catching up on reading, writing and arithmetic. Though it was the heat of summer, and there were other chores for them to do, they would be made available immediately.

The children who were to be Miss Jill's students were a hodgepodge of Italians, Polish, Irish, and Welsh. Most of their fathers were former miners, now scrambling for work where they could find it and farming their land for subsistence.

All the school children knew each other in this small town. Miss Jill had a class of 16 students, with ages ranging from 6 to 15. Because of the age disparity, she often had to prepare lesson plans independently.

For their part, the parents had strongly advised their children what an opportunity the teaching of Miss Jill presented, and that to disobey her would not be tolerated. Accordingly, the students, as a group, were polite, attentive, and fully aware of what the three R's could mean for them, and at the same time what a lack of attention would bring to them.

In the same serendipitous way that Miss Jill came to the children that summer, so Billy mysteriously arrived at her doorstep soon after she moved into the small white clapboard cottage on the edge of town which the town had provided her.

Billy was a large black and tan wolf-dog, with sharp, triangular ears and coal black eyes and large white teeth and fangs that protruded through his jowls. When Billy first appeared out of the hills, he watched Miss Jill from a distance just as she watched him. After a few days she began leaving food for him not too far from the cottage.

Over time, he came down from the hills at night and slept just outside her house by the abandoned chicken coop as if to protect her from predators. One night he eased his way through the open door into the kitchen, and lay down at her feet beneath the long wooden table where she got her school work done. It was a welcome improvement for both of them.

Soon after the arrival of Billy, the school children noticed that Miss Jill smiled more and seemed happier, and they wondered if maybe she had acquired a boyfriend, but it was Billy. They did not know why she called him Billy and no one asked her, as long as he made her happy. They liked their schoolmarm, not only for her school room tenacity and teaching them how to read and write, but also for her lessons on life, about doing the right thing and looking after each other, working hard and playing hard. It was almost like "The Word of the Lord" … without being too pushy … and they liked that too.

And they all grew to love Billy, that giant, black fur ball who accompanied Miss Jill to school each day and who seemed to tiptoe along behind her as if he were barely touching the ground, unless he took off after some varmint he spotted in the distance. Then he would return to his accustomed position, a few steps behind Miss Jill. Billy was not only light on his feet, but carried 110 pounds of "quick" if something or someone got between him and his mistress. Protecting her had become the primary mission in his life, and Miss Jill didn't seem to mind. And neither did the kids, who often jumped on Billy or pulled at his ears as he allowed himself to be wrestled to the ground. Billy did it all with only the occasional murmur of protest because the kids loved Miss Jill and he did, too.

One night, two brothers came to town by way of that same railroad line which had brought Miss Jill to Catchapea. They got off the train to get some whiskey and to look around and to get in some trouble if it were available. After a few drinks in the town's only bar, they wandered outside into the fading light. It was then that they spotted an attractive woman taking down her laundry in a little white cottage at the edge of town. After some observation, they determined that she probably lived alone except for a very large dog they saw in the front yard. They decided to pay her a visit.

As they snuck up to the house, the younger brother signaled to the other while he picked up a shovel which had been propped up against the side of the house. The older brother then confronted the dog who gathered himself to protect his house and his mistress, and, while he was so distracted, the younger brother came up from behind and wacked him on the head with the heavy metal shovel. Billy slumped to the ground, unconscious.

"There, that ought to do it," said the little brother as he laughed so hard he bent over.

"Who are you and why did you hurt my dog?" said Miss Jill as she appeared on the front porch and confronted the two men.

"So he wouldn't get in the way of our fun." A hard, hurtful laughter erupted from both of the brothers.

"She's a feisty one, ain't she," said the older brother.

Then to Miss Jill, he said, "Now get inside lady or I'll have to kill that big snot of a dog you've got over there." With that he stepped up on the porch and backed Miss Jill across the threshold and into the kitchen of the little cottage.

"You wait out there, Jerry," he yelled at his little brother. "Wait until I'm done — you be the lookout."

Jerry was annoyed by his assignment. He took out his pocket knife and began whittling furiously on a piece of wood while sitting on the edge of the front steps. He was otherwise not observant, and was not the lookout he should have been. For Billy had awakened. Jerry was totally unaware of the big black dog who sprang through the air and grabbed him with his jaws and teeth, pulled him to the ground, and shook him by the throat so he could not call out and until the blood ran out and drowned him in its wake. He was dead.

Next, Billy ran around to the side of the cottage where he heard the noise of a struggle. Immediate access was through the bedroom window. Billy shattered it in an instant as he hurled himself through it and saw the heavy arms that held his Mistress against her will. With teeth bared and a roar that filled the room, Billy crashed onto the man and began systematically tearing him apart. There was terror on the man's face. And there seemed nothing that Miss Jill could do to stop Billy from finishing his work. Her former accoster was screaming in the same terrifying tones that he must have caused in so many others. Now he was pleading for his own life.

"Let him go! Let him go!" said Miss Jill. "Don't kill him. No." Suddenly Billy stopped, emitting a low and menacing growl, but he did not follow the desperate man as he scrambled out the broken window, limping and bleeding. He disappeared into the wooded hills.

"He'll probably die out there," said Miss Jill. "Just as well." They walked through the kitchen and Miss Jill righted the wood table onto which the man had thrown her in his first attempts to rape her and before he dragged her into her bedroom. She picked up her school papers which had been scattered across the floor and put them back on the table and settled them neatly again.

Miss Jill sat down at the table and gave Billy an appreciative scratch behind the ears. "Well, Billy," she said tersely, "we've had quite a night, haven't we?"

The next day, a Saturday morning, Jill usually reserved for chores around the house. There was no school. On this particular Saturday morning, Miss Jill's first chore was to bury the younger brother deep in the ground. She used the same shovel which he had used to bash Billy the night before.

"How fitting," thought Miss Jill, as she labored to break through the clay and dig the hole. It took over an hour before she was able to dig a hole deep enough and to drag the body over to the grave and drop it in. She covered it up with the same dirt she had just unearthed, quickly filling in the grave over the body. The sweat of her work seeped through the light cotton dress she had put on that morning. She wiped her brow. Then she shook the dress to stop it from sticking to her.

During all this time, Billy stood sentry as he watched his mistress complete her task. He followed her from place to place as she found rocks to place upon the grave, enough rocks, she hoped, to prevent vultures and other varmints from getting at the body and exposing it for all to see. The fact that she had chosen a grave site beyond the work shed just a little way from the house would allow her to easily check the site from time to time to make sure it had not been disturbed.

Miss Jill was now sweating profusely. "Let's go to the pump, Billy," she said, "I could use some cool water. I'll bet you could too."

That same Saturday morning, Sheriff Joe Farley, a large middle-aged man with weathered face and crystal blue eyes, muscled arms and calloused hands, was riding through the hills just east of town where one of the townspeople thought one of his milking cows had run off. She was "in heat" and may have gone looking for a little romance. It was an enjoyable assignment for the sheriff, a good time to give his horse, Elmer, a little exercise.

He looked up to the sky and inhaled the early morning breeze already full of heat from the glowing sun. He scanned the horizon below when suddenly he saw buzzards circling something in the distance. It was probably the remains of an animal who had provided dinner for a mountain lion before the vultures had come to clean up. "Might even be that runaway milk cow," thought Sheriff Farley. "Better check it out." He gave Elmer a gentle prod with the side of his boots and they trotted off in the direction of the buzzards. A few minutes later, the vultures slowly and grudgingly scattered as Sheriff Farley and Elmer arrived on the scene.

Farley examined what looked like tooth bites on the grizzly remains of the body. He thought they may have been caused by a mountain lion as he first suspected, or even a wolf. But that was before he detected the trail of blood leading back towards town suggesting that whoever or whatever killed the man had begun there, not here in the wild.

Sheriff Farley tried to put the pieces of this mystery together, even as he rode slowly back towards town. He looked for other clues as he followed the direction of the blood trail. A few minutes later, he found himself almost directly in front of Miss Jill's house on the edge of town. He could already see a broken window on the side of the structure. He wondered if any of this had to do with those two strangers who had made themselves so obnoxious in town the night before and had said that, as brothers, they could lick anyone in town. Could one of them be the fellow he had discovered in the hills? And whatever happened to the other brother? Had they been at Miss Jill's cottage to cause her some kind of harm? And what would Billy have done to protect his mistress against two such drunken attackers?

Sheriff Farley walked around the property and noticed what appeared to be a freshly dug grave just beyond the shed. He saw what looked like boot marks which led to the very door of Miss Jill. And then he saw her standing in the front yard along with Billy. He got off his horse and walked it up to the front yard. "Well, good day, Miss Jill," he said, tipping his hat as he got off his horse. He gave Billy a little scratch behind the ears. "I bet Billy looks after you pretty good."

Miss Jill looked Sheriff Farley straight in the eye and said, "Yes, he does, Sheriff. I believe I would be lost without him."

"You know, Miss Jill, you may be right … might be right… err, lost without him that is." His voice drifted off. "Well, it feels like it's gonna be a hot one. Guess I'll go finish my chores early… Hey, I noticed what looks like a fresh grave over there behind the chicken coop. Anything I should know about?"

Again, Miss Jill looked directly at the Sheriff and said, "Not really, Sheriff. A fox tried to get at my chickens over there. Billy caught him and put him down. I thought it would be best to bury him pretty deep so that the buzzards wouldn't come calling."

Sheriff Farley picked up a sprig of honeysuckle and stuck it between his teeth. Then he pulled it out and put it up to his nose. "I love the smell of this stuff," he said. "It reminds me of the good things of summer." The sheriff hopped up on his horse and turned over his shoulder before departing. "By the way, I also noticed you have a broken bedroom window."

"Yes, Sheriff Farley, I've got to fix that." There was no explanation.

"Well, all right, Miss Jill, but while you're at it, I recommend you put more rocks on that grave. You never know when some hungry varmint might try to dig it up to get at that fox."

He tipped his hat again and looked down at the dog one more time. "Good boy, Billy. You keep looking after your mistress. I think she really needs you." Then he smiled at Miss Jill, shook the reins to let Elmer know it was time to go, and they trotted off.

Jill stooped to put her arms around Billy's shoulders as they watched the sheriff disappear towards the town center. It was going to be all right. The sheriff knew everything he needed or wanted to know.

As Sheriff Farley moved off, he had a couple of lingering questions about the trail of blood leading to Miss Jill's house, the broken window, and the "fox grave."

The sheriff thought to himself, "I reckon a lot of this had to do with an attack on Miss Jill by those two brothers, and that Billy had a lot to do with the demise of both of them. And I bet that broken window is what one of 'em jumped through to get away from Billy, only to bleed out up there in the hills.

"As for the fox grave, I bet the other brother must have ended up there, but I don't know how… just that Billy probably had a lot to do with that too. I figure I've already seen what his teeth and claws can do up in those hills."

Sheriff Farley's thoughts drifted off for a moment. Then he said to himself, "Maybe one day on down the road Miss Jill will tell me what actually happened − not now, but after I take off my sheriff's badge. For right now, I don't need to know any more. Justice has already been served as far as I'm concerned − but I think I'll be looking after Miss Jill and Billy a little bit more from now on."

## BART JONES OVERCOMES LIFE
*Getting Thrown Out*

Bart Jones was sneaking into his house by way of the open bedroom window. The window was about five feet above ground, and Bart grunted as he hoisted himself up and through the rectangular opening. He slithered head first down to the bedroom floor, then stood up. Something cold and wet was pushing against his hand. It turned out to be the nose of Bingo, the family Basset Hound. Bingo wagged his tail in salutation, then dropped to the floor and immediately fell asleep. Bart looked around in the semi darkness to the sheet covering the form of his wife sleeping on the bed. She was snoring gently, the quietest she ever got, thought Bart.

He smiled at the thought of his successful break-in to his own house. He silently slipped out of the bedroom, down the hallway, and into the kitchen. He opened the refrigerator door and grabbed a beer. He went into the next room, chugged the beer, and plopped down onto the living room couch, took one last swig to empty the can and squeezed it in half. He gently placed it on the floor as he rolled onto his back, looked up to the ceiling without contemplation and immediately fell asleep.

Sometime later he awoke, startled, as if from a bad dream.

One of us slept well, thought Bart as he sat up and looked over at the snoring form of Bingo still lying right next to him.

---

"Stay right there, Bart. I want to talk to you before you get up and sneak away." It was Helen, whom he had married five years ago when they were in love or at least 'in passion'. She was, it turned out, much more driven than Bart. She had graduated from Harvard Law School and was in her fifth year as an associate with the law firm of Abergrabie and Filch. She did corporate law and was good at it. She was up for partner. She was focused.

Bart was not, though he had acquired a Master's Degree in Creative Writing from New York University. In their five years of marriage, he had worked at a variety of jobs from high school teacher to salesman for Fuller Brush. He wanted to do his fair share while he wrestled with his writing. He was always working on something, usually some kind of veiled autobiography. Still, writing was his passion, his raison d'être, and for him that justified inadequacies in other areas. This is what Bart believed.

Helen did not, especially now that Bart had taken to staying out late and drinking too much.

"God, but you disgust me," said Helen.

Obviously this wasn't going to go well, thought Bart.

"I want a divorce," said Helen tapping a high heeled shoe which led up to her sculpted legs. Hers was a diva perfect profile, completed by a small waist and perky breasts. Helen had a chiseled jaw and piercing blue eyes, all framed by a tight page boy cut of thick black hair.

Intimidating as ever, thought Bart.

He thought quickly, "A divorce, huh?" said Bart.

"I don't know if you've thought about this, Helen," said Bart, thinking quickly. "I could ask for a lot of alimony, what with you being the main breadwinner in this family. Ah, thank God for women and equal rights," he smiled.

"Oh, get dressed and get out, Bart. Otherwise, I'll get a court order to attach everything you own. I bought the house, so forget that. You can keep that fifteen year old rust bucket you drive, and you can take Bingo, that flatulent old flea bag. I'm allergic to him anyway."

### Bart Jones Gets a Job

Bart was content with Bingo in his one level studio apartment. There was a small kitchen which resembled a club car with a Formica tabletop counter and three big stools on the other side all of which were visible from his bedroom and living room because they were the same. Cozy, but it worked.

There was no one else but Bingo, and Bart didn't anticipate any guests. Still, he wondered why he was always looking from the outside in. He had reached a point with himself that he had come to accept this perception, even to prefer his own company and his dog's over the "in crowd" anxiety of everyone else. It really was quite freeing that he no longer yearned for acceptance or approval or even inclusion and was happy just to be directly connected to himself.

In some way, this insouciance, an active willingness to show no desire to measure up or be accepted, actually created a groundswell of respect, even admiration for his stance of going it alone and being happy to be apart. Since he no longer felt the need for approval by the crowd as they did of each other, this actually created an inside-out respect for Bart.

And for those few who were tired of the rat race and the struggles related to it, he believed some people might actually wish that they could lead their lives more like him. This gave Bart a certain amount of satisfaction even as he knew it was time to move on with his life.

His writing was at a standstill, but he had just had something published in the Letters to the Editor department in the local paper, so that was something. It was a source in which to publish and certainly to vent. The subject of his first letter was 'The Actual Inequality of Equal Justice Under the Law.' It made him angry, so this outlet on behalf of the little guy was heartening.

Having said that, he had no idea how he was going to pay the rent that was already overdue. With no immediate solution, he decided to write another letter to the paper. The subject of this letter was "The Diminution of the Word *Heroes,*" how the military and civilian media had taken to calling all soldiers heroes, not just veterans. What did that do to the psyche of the real heroes, the ones who had earned bronze stars, silver stars, the ones who had risked their lives for their comrades or even died for their country? There are many vets, and that's an honorable thing. But there are only a few heroes and their ultimate contributions should never be diminished or diluted.

Bart had followed this up with yet another letter to the editor which attacked military euphemisms. It condemned clinical referrals to indiscriminate killings of innocent people by misplaced bombs as collateral damage. A day later this was followed by a fourth letter which addressed 'The Tyranny of Organized Religion over Individual Beliefs.'

Within a couple of days, Bart received an email from this same newspaper. Much to his surprise, he was informed that all four letters were going to be published within the next month. It was more than he had hoped for, and he was quite pleased. Bart felt by some skewed personal measurement he had now begun to validate his worth as a writer. Still, there was the ongoing problem of the rent due at the end of the month and that was only 10 days away. Talk about collateral damage…

The phone rang. It was his first call in a week and he had no idea whom it might be from, so he answered tentatively, "Hello?"

"Is this Bart Jones?" the voice said.

Bart Jones feared this was yet another bill collector calling because he only got calls from bill collectors. He remained silent.

Undeterred, the caller continued. "Okay, I think I can hear you breathing in the background. My name is Bill Dicks and I'd like to talk to you right away."

"About what?" Bart was still suspicious.

"About writing a column for my newspaper, The Daily News and Dispatch. You know, the one you keep sending your letters to."

"So, what is it you do for your newspaper that you want me to write for?" said Bart.

"I'm the Managing Editor, and I have the authority to hire you if you work out. Interested?"

"Uh, yes sir," *Interested?* thought Bart. *He doesn't know how desperately interested I am.*

"Can you come down to the newspaper tomorrow at 10:00?"

"Well, let me check my appointment book…" which he knew was blank.

"Uh, sure, I can make it."

"And bring any new ideas with you. They seem to stir up a lot of interest, pro and con, and that's what my newspaper likes, because that's what sells newspapers. So, we'll talk. Okay?"

"Okay."

"Oh, by the way," said Bill Dicks, "in this day and age of separation and divorce, we'd really like to produce a series of articles that probe the lives of separated and divorced people…the problems and solutions… the accommodations, expensive lawyers…we want all of that stuff for our readers information and excitement. Everybody likes a good divorce story… warts and all. Can you come up with something like that, Bart?"

"Well," smiled Bart, looking down at Bingo and thinking of Helen, "I sure can."

"Can you bring it tomorrow when you come in?" said Bill Dicks.

"No problem," said Bart, still thinking of Helen. "I have personal experience. I can certainly get that piece to you by tomorrow. Warts and all… a lot of warts."

"Good," said Bill Dicks, "that's just the stuff I am looking for. Now you bring that article to me tomorrow, and I will give you an advance of 500 dollars. Does that work for you?"

"Does it ever?" said Bart. "I would go through divorce all over again just to get you that true-life story."

"I bet you would," said Bill Dicks.

"You should," said Bill as they said goodbye.

"You know," Bart said, looking down at Bingo again, "I can't wait to tell Helen I am finally getting something out of the marriage; in addition to you, old boy."

Bart and Bingo went into the kitchen. Bart opened the refrigerator door, pulling out a large bone for Bingo and a king-sized Budweiser for himself. They settled down back in the living room and turned on the television, only to find it showing Jimmy Stewart in *It's a Wonderful Life*. Bart took a long draft and lay back on the floor next to Bingo in celebration of their new life.

### Instant Karma

Someone was knocking on his door, probably the apartment manager demanding the rent which was way overdue.

"All right, all right," said Bart talking through the closed door.

"You'll get your rent at the end of this week. Just give me a break, will ya?"

The knocking continued. Louder.

"Bart, it's me, Helen. I want to talk to you. Now let me in."

Bart watched the doorknob jiggle. *What does she want now?* He mused. *She can't get anything more out of me. She knows I don't have any money, and she certainly does not want Bingo, not that he would want to go back. Me either.*

"Let me in or I will break the door down. Come on Bart, I really need to talk to you."

She was actually pleading, thought Bart. Highly unusual for her, plus it sounds like she probably would beat the door down.

Slowly, Bart turned the door latch, unlocking the door, and Helen came bursting through.

Standing there in her high heel stilettos and form-fitting jacket and skirt cut well above the knee — all this put Bart on the alert. It also reminded him that he had not been with a woman in quite awhile.

But remember, he reminded himself, this is not "any woman" — this is Helen — the original ballbreaker.

Bingo had already taken shelter under the kitchen counter while Bart parked himself on a kitchen stool in front of it. He sat down casually with one leg pushed down on a cross strut, the other reaching out casually to the floor.

He hoped this would give him a look of confidence.

Somewhat like a heat seeking missile, Helen stopped her advance to take a look around. "God, Bart, this place is a mess." She ran a finger over the gathering dust on Bart's microwave oven which also was caked with a little cream and marmalade left over from several breakfasts. Bart watched Helen as she picked up a glass from the pile of dirty dishes in the sink. Then she picked up a couple of empty beer cans and deposited them in the wastebasket which she had found under the counter behind Bart. She then turned to him and sighed deeply.

"Are you working for the sanitation police?" asked Bart mildly. He waited for one of Helen's patented barbed responses.

He got none. "I want you back, Bart."

For once Bart, the writer, the man of swift retorts, said nothing. He was in shock. This was the last thing he expected… and it terrified him.

He had just built this shaky foundation of independence and had found solitude for his writing and he even had found partnership in a good and loyal, though flatulent partner.

He felt threatened by Helen. It meant, if she wanted him back, she must have a reason and Bart knew that if she wanted him back she would fight to get him back… and Bart did not want that. He knew how good she was at getting her way. He had to stay strong.

He decided to lead with the obvious: "Helen, you could not possibly want me back, or Bingo. You kicked me out because I drink too much and I don't bring in any money and that is a perfectly good reason to have kicked me out and I have accepted it in full. Now you know, I am committed to my writing and quite possibly all of my old habits. I have not changed. What could you possibly want with me?"

"I know, Bart. It's crazy, but I miss you terribly. Let's give it another chance and I will try to be more flexible. Just get rid of Bingo, I am allergic to him and he makes me sneeze. You can drop him off at the SPCA. They will take care of him and you can come on home."

Helen turned away, held her nose, and then turned back to Bart.

"And God does he smell. I know he can't help it, Bart, but we've really got to get rid of him."

"We! You said we! When did we become we again, Helen?" Now Bart knew that there was something else she wanted from him.

He stood up and scratched his backside where he had located an imaginary itch.

Bart did this sometimes when he was thinking. He also knew it annoyed Helen. That was a bonus.

Helen began tapping her stiletto shoe on Bart's circa 1950 parquet floor. She was impatient.

"Alright, Helen," said Bart, "you're holding out. What's really on your mind? I know from bitter experience when you've got an agenda. Bingo and I have things to do, so just spit it out."

"Sure you've got things to do… like watching an old rerun of Gunsmoke. Well, you're no Matt Dillon."

"Ah," said Bart, "now that's the caustic, old, demeaning Helen I have come to know, the real Helen."

"Okay, okay, Bart. I was trying to be nice, but I guess I couldn't stand to have you and Bingo home anyway. But, I do have something great for the both of us. Just listen to me for a moment. You remember my uncle, Herman Hardick. He walked out on my Aunt Mimsey and three weeks later, died of a heart attack while in bed with a twenty-five year old hooker. Apparently, his last words were, "Well, if you gotta go…""

"No wonder I loved your Uncle Herman," he interrupted Helen. "Now, please make your point. Bingo needs to go out."

"Alright, alright," said Helen. "I'll tell you the whole story. Before he died unexpectedly, that old geezer left me a cashier check for $25,000 just as he did for five other nieces and nephews. I guess he knew he was gonna go and he wanted to leave us something."

"So, what's your problem, Helen? You should be ecstatic… and why would I care?" he said slowly.

"Oh, well, it's a minor problem. In his incompetence Uncle Herman must have made out my check in both of our names by mistake. He is my blood relative and you know he would want that money to come to me. So, if you'll just endorse the back of the check, I'll pay your rent this month. You have no money, so I am sure it's overdue." This as she pulled the check out from her black Hermes purse and thrust it under his nose. "Just sign here and I'll be out of your hair."

At first, Bart felt like a fish trapped in a barrel. And that is what Helen wanted. But then, the fireworks of cognition exploded in his head.

"Not so fast, Helen. You can't get your money until my signature is on that check and you know why. I am a co-beneficiary and am just as entitled as you to that money. Therefore, we will have to make arrangements to split it, won't we?"

One of Helen's famous ear piercing screams filled the apartment, even waking up poor Bingo from a deep sleep.

There was an eerie silence. Then, Helen spoke in a carefully measured cadence. Her eyes flashed, a vein was visibly throbbing from her neck. Bart waited for another explosion, like the time a few years ago when Helen threw a sharp-edged silver candlestick holder that he had dodged as it impaled itself on the wall behind him. He knew he had to be careful.

Another big sigh, then, "Alright, Bart. I knew you'd be a bastard about this even though I have supported you all these years." She was right, in a way, Bart supposed. But he also knew he had paid for it in many other demeaning ways.

A third heavy silence was followed by yet another Helen sigh. Bart knew Helen hoped his sense of guilt and general cowardice might combine to make him acquiese.

"Alright, Bart," said Helen. "Let's get this over with. You sign Uncle Herman's check here and I'll write you a check for $12,500 from my own account."

A smile crept over Bart's face. This was her backup strategy — get him to sign Herman's check, write me a check on her account, and then stop payment on it before he could get to the bank to cash it — thus leaving her with the money and Bart, nothing.

"Now, Helen, there is only one way I sign off on this check. And that is if we go to the bank together where we will cash the check together before a banker's eyes. Half the money coming to me, half to you. Deal?"

"You are such an ungrateful bastard."

"Good," he said. "I'll go get my coat and we'll go. I can walk Bingo when I get back."

One hour later, with $12,500 deposited into Bart's own banking account and the added bonus of Helen telling him to never knock on her door again, he returned to his own apartment to find Bingo wagging his tail a couple of times in welcome, before falling back asleep.

Bart quickly took Bingo out for a quick potty break. Once back in the apartment he considered what he would do with his windfall. Fix his car so it would pass inspection. Step up to a better apartment. Buy Bingo a new doggie bed. And, in a fit of uncharacteristic maturity, Bart decided he might even start a small savings account.

When Bart arrived at the Daily News and Dispatch to meet with the managing director the next day, he knew indeed that he had a very good divorce story. It was full of warts and included the story of how he managed to get his share of Uncle Herman's inheritance check from his estranged wife. He was sure it would be well received. He was going to call it the "Art of Divorce and Keeping your Dog at the Same Time."

Life was good. In fact, it had just become so much better thanks to Helen's Uncle Herman, certainly for Bingo, and in a fully unintended way, to his soon to be former wife, Helen.

It was probably a good thing that good ol' addled Uncle Herman had never gotten to know Bingo, thought Bart. Otherwise, he probably would have given all of his money to Bingo.

# GIRL IN THE WINDOW

It was early morning, clear, and there was a warming sun. I sat at an al fresco table of the Café Michel, my pen hovering over a legal yellow pad as I watched the girl across the street. She was staring into a window as if to gaze at the half-dressed mannequins on display. Perhaps she was looking at her own reflection. She carefully removed a strand of hair from her forehead. Abruptly she turned as if to confront me. I realized, too late, that she had also seen *my* reflection in the window.

She crossed the street and stood before me. "Why were you looking at me?" she said with a small smile.

Startled, but only for a moment, I resorted to candor. "I didn't see anyone else to look at and I was drawn by your vision in the window. I'm sorry."

"Oh, all right then," said the girl as she sat down across from me at my table. "You are probably lonely. I've still got a few minutes before work. Why don't you buy me a latté?"

I could only wonder at my good luck. She was beautiful, she had a radiant smile and the figure of the mannequins she dressed in the window. She laughed gently as a breeze blew her hair in my direction. I laughed too, the first time in a long time.

"So where do you work?" I asked.

"Why, at that same clothing store just across the way. That is our display window you saw me examining. I dress those mannequins every day before work, and I look at them very carefully from the outside to determine what will look best for the mood of the day.

"And what did you think I was doing," she continued, "just gazing at my own reflection?"

"Well, I guess I did," I said sheepishly.

Again, this beautiful girl produced that gentle laugh. "Well, I was doing that, too. I am a girl you know. Now will you buy me a latté?"

I signaled to the waiter, who came and took the order.

"By the way, I own that shop," she continued. "I need to get the mannequins ready before opening time, and so I dress them every day, right about now. If it is on your schedule, why don't you come again sometime and I'll buy *you* a latté."

"I prefer black coffee," I said, smiling.

"Black coffee it is," she said. "And what do you do? You have me at a disadvantage."

"Well, I'm a writer."

"Hmm. Well, come anyway." She laughed and was gone.

---

The good thing about being a freelance writer, I thought, was that I had a flexible schedule, sometimes too flexible. Still, it meant I could go to the Café Michel two days in a row.

The next morning I sat at the same table as yesterday, superstitious I guess. I looked across the street with the hope of seeing the girl in the window. She was not there.

I did, however, see the corpulent figure of a man who appeared to be the owner of the café. He was simultaneously directing a bus boy while scowling at a waiter he had decided was chatting too long with a customer. "Hey Louis, you've got other customers besides the pretty ones. Let's get moving," he said.

He came over to me and continued to make his point. "Monsieur, you see how lazy these young people are. No sense of pride. As you may have guessed, I am Henri, the owner." He bowed and his belly spilled over his apron. "If I did not watch them like a hawk, they would never bus their tables, and what a mess the café would look."

He pulled up his food-stained apron to wipe his perspiring face. I decided to respond to his position in kind with the hope that he would be receptive to mine. "Well, I do see your point," I began dispassionately, "but, say, I have a question if you don't mind."

"Certainly, monsieur," said Henri, thinking he had found a sympathetic ear. "How can I help you?"

"Do you know that young girl who appeared yesterday in front of the window across the street? I believe she was arranging the window display for her shop."

The café owner paused, wiped his mouth with his apron again, and cleared his throat. "Monsieur, I must inform you the girl that you ask about does not actually arrange that window display, nor does she even work in that shop. She does arrive almost every morning and appears to do so, even as she appears to be doing her hair in the reflection in the window."

"I don't understand," I said.

"Ah, I will explain it to you, monsieur." Henri continued with a knowing smile. "She is not what she seems, not at all. She only pretends. Of course she is harmless and she always goes home…"

"Where is her home?" I interrupted. I was confused, upset that this beautiful girl who had come into my life so suddenly was not who I thought she was.

"Ah, so that is what you want to know, monsieur. Our girl in the window resides at St. Gertrude's Sanctuary. It is a mental asylum, but it is really quite nice. It is run by Catholic nuns, and they're all quite a fine group, sympathique, you know. I've never had any problems with them, not even with residents who are paroled out from time to time to do a little walk about. She lives over there," said Henri, pointing to a large gray building, somewhat gothic in nature, about three blocks away.

I sat there stunned. I could think of nothing to say.

"Monsieur, do not despair," said Henri, the café owner. "She will come back tomorrow or the next day, and you will see her, and if she sees you and recognizes you, she may come over and sit at your table, just as I saw her doing yesterday."

I thanked Henri for his information and, as I had already paid my bill, I began walking in the general direction of St. Gertrude's Sanctuary. I don't know what compelled me to go there in search of the girl in the window, but somehow seeing her once again seemed important to me. I didn't know why. Maybe she was just a kaleidoscopic mirage. I needed to make sense of it all.

I arrived at the sanctuary and knocked on the front door. I was met by a little round woman dressed in a nun habit. I estimated she was about 70 years old. She identified herself as Mother Beatrice, the Reverend Mother Superior of the Sanctuary. She knew from my description exactly whom I was seeking. She smiled at me and said, "Yes, that is our Leah. She has an active imagination. You seem like a nice young man. Are you Catholic? No. Well, no matter. Would you like to see her?"

When I nodded yes, Mother Beatrice continued. "But remember, she may not know you. Her memory comes and goes." Mother Beatrice turned to me again before leaving to have Leah brought up from her room. "Why don't you wait right over there in our morning room where we get lots of sun."

There were two sofas facing each other and several chairs by a window where the sun was shining through. I sat down in one of the arm chairs and looked out at a beautiful flower garden where I observed a couple of youngish nuns working the soil. Then I heard footsteps and looked up to see Leah striding across the front hall in my direction, her black hair gently flowing as she moved purposefully towards me. She smiled and sat in the chair across from me. She was completely at ease.

"You look vaguely familiar," she said. "Do I know you?"

"Yes," I said slowly. "We talked yesterday at the café across from the window you were dressing."

"Oh," she said. "Was that yesterday? I don't remember much about yesterday, but yes, I do that window almost every day, when I can get away from here." She smiled and stood up looking so elegant, her black dress gently tracing the curves of her body. She started to walk away and then turned to say, "I still don't remember you. It must have been yesterday." She smiled again. "À bientôt." Then she disappeared down the hallway.

Mother Beatrice reappeared just as I was getting up to leave. "Well, I guess you have perceived by now that Leah is beautiful and personable, but she has a very unreliable memory, the result of a car accident years ago. When the doctor determined that her memory was such that not even her parents could take care of her, they brought her to us. A sweeter mademoiselle you'll never meet, but she can go nowhere alone."

"What about the daily window dressing and the café?" I asked.

"Yes, she does go there almost every day. It gives her happiness, but there's always one of us quietly watching nearby to make sure she finds her way home. It is her little piece of reality, of independence… as much as we are able to give her."

I thanked Mother Beatrice, and she replied, "Come back whenever you like. Who knows, she may recognize you the next time." I smiled and turned away.

I knew I would not come back. I could not impose my reality upon hers, a reality built upon happiness, hers and the nuns who helped her to have it.

I smiled at the thought of her innocent joy. But I knew I could not be a part of her world. My own reality covered me up and could only destroy hers. Still, I decided I could, on occasion, go to the Café Michel and perhaps I would see her pretend to dress the window, and maybe she would recognize me … maybe she would walk across the street and sit at my table … and maybe she would ask me for a latté.

## PUBLISHING WITH JOHN GRISHAM

I was standing behind the podium at Boar's Head Inn, a premium resort and meeting destination in Charlottesville, Virginia. I did a reading from my latest book *Killing Time in a Small Southern Town*. It is historical fiction which tells of the kidnapping and attempted murder of two African American boys by two white boys during the pre-integration struggle of the early 1960s in Charlottesville.

I was speaking to an audience of approximately 45 and was hopeful of having a lively discussion and perhaps sell 25 to 30 books. By comparison, I had done a reading the previous week at the Batesville Market, a beautiful old hardware store circa 1920s that had recently been restored. There, I had presented to a group of fifteen, eight of whom were friends of mine. They had already bought my book so that left a sales market of seven, of which two had checked the book out from their local libraries. Of the remaining five, three left early to complete their grocery shopping, and one of the last two actually purchased a book. This produced a grand total of one book sold. Nevertheless, there was enthusiastic conversation and discussion. Such is my world of marketing books, self-publishing and tilting at windmills.

I have always hoped that discussion and praise for my books, together with the occasional query letter, would not only yield more book sales but somehow lead to the world of big-time publishers. That was always my hope. And I always come back to the story of the little boy and his father walking along the beach:

There was a large group of beached starfish who had been washed ashore and the boy asked his father what would happen to them.

"Well, they'll all probably die," his father said.

The little boy picked up one of the starfish and threw it back into the water. When his father asked him what he was doing, the boy said he was saving the starfish. The father smiled and said, "Well, you can't save them all."

"Well, I saved that one," the boy said.

In the same way, I hoped that some big publishing company would pluck my query fish from amongst the thousands of rejected ones all around. They would nourish it and ultimately publish the intended book for its millions of readers.

These were the subliminal thoughts that raced through my head even as I fielded questions and comments from my audience at the Boar's Head Inn. They did seem to like my book. For me, that always produced a temporary "rush" soon to be followed by recurrent doubts of what had I really accomplished.

But wait! In that very moment, on that very night, I experienced a totally unexpected breakthrough. I had just acknowledged a member of the audience who had raised her hand at the end of the reading. She was an attractive blonde-haired woman who appeared to be in her 50s. She stood up and said that she loved my book, *Killing Time*, and was going to show it to her husband because she believed it deserved to be presented to a much larger audience. She identified herself as Renée Grisham, wife of John Grisham, the author. She said she was going to ask him to read it to see if he liked it as much as she did.

*Wow! Maybe my time has finally come*, I thought.

Three days later, John Grisham himself called to say that he too loved my book and wanted to get together to discuss it. He asked me if I would like to join him for the upcoming UVA basketball game against Duke. He had an extra seat for that game and he knew from reading my bio that I was a UVA graduate and would probably like that.

"Yes, I would."

The following Saturday I found myself sitting next to John Grisham on the "floor" of the John Paul Jones Arena. Grisham was a middle-aged man with piercing blue eyes and receding blonde hair. He was fit and relaxed and charmingly disarming, and his were the best seats in the house. We sat in the front row "on the floor" only a few feet away from the players. Right in front of me, was phenomenon Kihei Clark, UVA's diminutive point guard. And next to him was Mamadi Diakite, the 6"9' Grand Orange.

They were so close I could see the sweat dripping from their bodies. And three seats down from me sat the lanky, silver-haired Terry Holland, perhaps UVA's most famous coach. He was talking to Ralph Sampson, who was seated to his immediate right. This is the same 7'4" Ralph Sampson who was perhaps the greatest UVA basketball player of all time.

Oh, what a night.

Meanwhile, Grisham and I talked and kibitzed while cheering on UVA to a thrilling 52-50 nail-biting victory over the Duke Blue Devils. After the game, Coach Tony Bennett came over to shake hands with John Grisham. They apparently knew each other well.

When Grisham introduced me as a "fellow author," Tony put his hand on my shoulder and said, "It's an honor to meet any fellow author of John Grisham. I love his books and I'll be looking for yours."

After the game, we had drinks at a local restaurant during which time John said he was going to do what he could to get his agent to take on my book. "It reminds me so much of some of my books. I almost wish I had written it myself." At the end of this wonderful evening, John shook my hand warmly and reiterated that he would have his agent read *Killing Time* and get back to me in the near future.

This was all exceptional news for my writing career. My wife Marjorie seemed just as excited as I was. I could barely contain my anticipation of being published by Doubleday and Company. I could see the national book tours, the interviews on the Today Show, a one-on-one interview on the Tonight Show and even a major book review from the New York Times.

Finally, at the age of 73, I would have the opportunity to be "discovered overnight." Finally, I would have the vehicle to showcase my writing talent and provide me with the publishing success I had so long sought... *and so richly deserved*, I thought.

Time went by, first days and then weeks, and then a month. Had it all been a fantasy? Suddenly an email appeared on my computer. It was from John Grisham apologizing for his agent not getting back to me sooner, something about a scheduling conflict, but that he would make sure that he did so in the next day or so at the most. *The dream lives*, I thought.

Grisham's parting comment was, "Go Hoos."

Again, days went by and then weeks. Nothing. I sat at my desk, gazing out the window looking at some ducks floating on the small watery cove which touched on my back yard. At this moment I imagined that any query fish I might throw into the water today would not be rescued by Double Day Publishing. In fact, it would probably be eaten by the ducks or simply slip under the surface, never to be seen again. So much for big-time publishing.

Then the phone rang. It was J. J. Snerdley, literary agent for John Grisham at Double Day Publishing.

"At John Grisham's firm request," he said, "I have read your book, *Killing Time in a Small Southern Town*. Mr. Bigelow, *Killing Time* is really quite a good read. It has a great plot-line, the characters are well developed and the action is scintillating. I don't want to overuse the cliché, but it's a real page turner."

"That's terrific," I interjected.

"Well, I suppose it is," said Snerdley. "However, there is one hitch. Your book reads very much like many of Mr. Grisham's books. In some ways it's better than some of his books. That's why I can't accept your book for publication. It's simply too good. You get my meaning, right, Mr. Bigelow?"

"Well, not exactly," I began. Snerdley interrupted my comments and cascading emotions. "You see, Mr. Bigelow, it simply wouldn't be good business to put a book like yours out there which might actually compete with John's books. You understand that would not be good for John. So, regretfully, I must tell you that we can't take you on. But I do think WTF Publications might be interested. Why don't you query them? It is a good book so keep on doing what you're doing. I'm sure one of those queries will work out for such a good book. By the way, I understand you are an alumnus of UVA."

"Yes," I said weakly.

"Well, as John would say, GO HOOS. Bye, bye for now."

---

Okay, fellow writers. **Spoiler Alert**.

This was all a daydream conflated by my fevered imagination. It is nothing more than a cautionary tale about putting too much hope or expectation of having a major publishing company accept your book for publication. Of course, there is always that possibility, but for 99% of us, it is not to be a reality.

Of course, you should continue sending out queries and exploring all levels of publication, but you should appreciate all victories, all levels of success along the way. Embrace the process. It's fundamentally about advancing *your* writing.

Do the best you can in the writing arena every day. Respect your writing — work at it every day — whether you write a chapter of blinding brilliance or a couple of fragmentary sentences which you know you will rewrite the next day.

Do make sure you use all the publishing avenues open to you. Create interviews in the local newspapers or weeklies. Pursue interviews with the local radio and television outlets. Do as many readings as you can secure in writer's clubs, book clubs and service clubs. Enjoy them. They provide such a great arena to discuss your book … your writing.

Be hopeful. Reach for the winning query starfish. Remember, there's only one John Grisham but there's only one you… and your writing is unique to you.

Help others help you. Never give up. Keep writing. You already *own* that success … because you … are a writer.

# THE JAMES DEAN FANTASY

*Camera close up on young man lying face up in bed. Near dawn lighting. Man appears to be in that dormant state in which he is no longer completely asleep but not yet completely conscious. The man's inner voice is our narrator. The dream-like scenes recreate his memory of the night before.*

Another Sunday morning waking dream ... I lie in bed with eyes half closed and recall last night's party. It had been the usual crowd plus a few new faces. There was jazzy music you could dance to but didn't, and plenty to eat and drink.

Booze — as usual I guess I had a little too much, more than a buzz but less than drunk. I always knew when to go home. I said my goodbyes and headed for my car.

Driving home was always easy. My old turbo 940 Volvo could practically drive itself — by radar you might say.

I remembered driving fast on that first twisting rise of Old Stony Point Road. I look up to the evergreens in the foothills of the Blue Ridge Mountains on the left, and down to the newly cut hay fields on the right, all lit by a bright three-quarter moon.

I gunned the Volvo on the straightaway I knew so well. Anticipating the sharp curve to the right, I speed shifted to third in order to have the necessary power to pull out as I hit the center of the curve.

I was living the *James Dean Fantasy*. That's how I always felt on this stretch of the road after a good Saturday night.

"Live hard, die young and leave a beautiful memory." I chuckled inwardly as I recalled this part of my waking dream. It was a little immature, but what the hell, it felt good and it was harmless.

I can't remember what happened next. I can't remember the rest of the drive home. Wait. Maybe I drank too much to remember. I've got to watch that.

> *The camera refocuses on the man's face. The light turns 'hospital harsh' as the camera pulls away to reveal he is actually lying in a hospital bed and has a doctor in green scrubs and a nurse in white for company. Their clinical approach, the stark whiteness of the hospital room, contrast with the soft dreamlike sequences we have seen until now.*

I opened my eyes. Was I awake or was I still dreaming? I saw that the doctor now has put on a surgical mask and he was talking with the nurse. I could hear their voices.

"Another boy racer, nurse. Yeah. He must have tried to straighten out that S-turn on Rt. 20 once too often. What? Yeah, he'd been drinking all right ... Probably thought he was James Dean. The difference is James Dean only killed himself.

"Apparently, he crossed the center line just enough to clip a little sports car and drive it straight into a tree. Young married couple. Both killed instantly. Maybe they're lucky. This fellow is paralyzed from the neck down. We don't know yet if he can see or hear but that really doesn't matter. There appears to be substantial brain damage and he'll never walk again ... or talk. He's pretty much a vegetable. Maybe that's just as well for him. He'll never know what he's done."

> *Close-up of man's face, then to super close-up of his darting, blinking eyes. Live conscious terror is apparent.*

But, I do hear you. I do understand you. I blink and try to wake up. God, make this a dream. I scream but I make no sound. God, I am alive. Oh, God! Let me be dead. Let me be dead like James Dean.

## A FIRESIDE CHAT

*Edward Coles vs. Thomas Jefferson, James Madison,*
*and James Monroe on the subject of slavery and emancipation.*

This is Edward Coles. I am now 65 and looking back on my life. Perhaps this will be a good memoir for my descendants, if no one else. In particular, I would like to talk about my 1814 fireside chat with three presidents at Monticello, all my lifelong mentors and all who wished to dissuade me from my crusade to go to the free territory of Illinois and emancipate my slaves. It was the crusade that dominated my life.

Let me tell you how it all began.

### A Ride up Monticello Mountain

It was a cool, August early evening in 1814. There had been good rain for the growing season, the fields were full of healthy plantings, and the trees of the woods I rode through were lush with leaves hanging from heavy laden branches.

I slowed my horse to a trot and then a slow walk as I passed by Michie Tavern where, occasionally, I had shared a draft with Colonel Monroe. I knew I would see him tonight. In fact, I had been invited to an intimate dinner by Thomas Jefferson himself, that also would include my mentor and current employer, President James Madison.

The circumstances were incredible, that I, far younger than all three, I was 28 and Monroe, I believe, in his mid 50's while President Madison I knew was 63. Jefferson himself, the sage of Monticello, was said to be over 70. I couldn't believe that it was important enough to them that they would want to talk to me about my plans to take my slaves to Illinois, a free territory, in order to free them. I knew they wanted to dissuade me from this project. That would be the overall purpose of our meeting tonight.

I had talked to or corresponded with them all about my decision and I knew they were troubled by it. It was not because it was my conviction – they supported that – just not now. They felt it was not the right time. They were all not only my friends but had been my mentors since I was a child. I envied their every accomplishment, I respected them above all else, save my overriding conviction to emancipate my slaves now.

In fact, I had planned to free my slaves when first I inherited them and a small farm in 1809, but circumstances, including my service to James Madison during his presidency, have prevented me from doing so until now. But now, it had become an overriding force in my psyche. It is true that many of the plantation owners where I grew up had long talked of the anathema of slavery. They all agreed that it should be ended in time, but they also agreed that there were problems that needed to be resolved before this could happen.

Philosophically, many plantation owners believed that slaves were inferior mentally and could not survive on their own and would not be able to handle their newly freed status.

Another more practical fear was that some might come back to murder their previous owner for his cruelty towards them – certainly not Jefferson, Madison, nor Monroe, who were known to be considerate to the welfare of their slaves.

But the best known and least acknowledged reason for withholding emancipation was that the whole agrarian economy of Virginia and other slaveholding states was wholly dependent on slave labor. It was feared the economy would totally collapse without slavery.

Another reason – it was feared these hundreds of thousands of freed slaves would soon outnumber the white population. Would they be willing to work for small wages and "stay in their place?"

It is absolutely true that Jefferson, Madison, and Monroe believed in eventual emancipation. Slavery, they knew was a moral stain on the very core of democracy. If freedom of the individual was everything, then the basis of our entire representative government and our republic is basically illegitimate, until the institution of slavery is forever ended.

I knew from previous correspondence with Jefferson that he would want to wait for another generation, my generation, to resolve the problem even as it was our obligation to convince the general white population to go along with this concept. I feared his line of reasoning would simply delay freedom, generation after generation, by pragmatics alone.

Someone had to be the pioneer. Someone had to be willing to sacrifice everything to end slavery. I believed with all my heart that this was my calling.

As I crested the last hill, I could see a house rise in the distance. I looked down to the valley to Charlottesville and beyond on up to the very mountains of the Blue Ridge that seemed to merge into the sky. I knew again why Jefferson would choose the planting of his house and farm high up on this mountain land where the earth was less fertile and so many small hills and valleys presented continual challenges to planting and plowing. In the face of these obstacles, Jefferson had chosen the most beautiful view anywhere, and for him, that trumped anything else – beauty, aesthetics – such was his vision.

And there he was himself, the long and graceful figure of Jefferson, standing on the steps as I approached that house, a beautiful Palladian structure. It was known as Monticello. I did not know what was going to happen now, but I must explain to this august company that I would free my slaves with or without their blessing.

As I dismounted, Jefferson spoke, "Welcome, my dear, young friend. You must be thirsty after your ride. Let me take you to the veranda. Madison is there. In fact, he is staying the night, as he usually does when he comes to Monticello, and of course, Colonel Monroe is there, he is early for everything."

Jefferson chuckled as he led me around the house to the terraced veranda. Here began one of one of the most fascinating, delightful, but frustrating and saddening evenings I have ever known.

### The Veranda

It was almost like a dream for me. Another beautiful, cool August evening as the temperature customarily drops from the mountains at the end of the day.

Our initial conversation moved quickly from the beauty of the night to the current war with the English that was threatening the very existence of our country; a country which, at that time, was fewer than 40 years old.

Jefferson, now in his seventies, spoke first.

He was dressed in his customary gray surtout (cover all) coat. Underneath he wore a frayed red waistcoat and long, gray pantaloons tapering to his white woolen stockings. It was as if he chose comfortable clothes over elegance, yet still his long, lean figure and a face projecting grace and wisdom could be seen through his crystal blue eyes.

Jefferson looked to Madison. "And so, my friend, is it true the British Army is about to debark from their warship on the Baltimore River to attack us by land? If so, will they march towards Baltimore or do you think it is possible they might try to invade our very capital? I wish that you and our neighbor and friend here, Colonel Monroe, can give myself and young Mr. Coles here, the particulars of this current threat to our country's life and liberty."

Jefferson put his arm around my shoulder as we waited for Madison, our current President, to speak.

He was quiet as he slowly turned from the view he had of the mountain to the valley below to face us all. This great man, for whom I was even now working as private secretary in Washington City, was himself dressed in his customary outfit – black coat, black breeches, and silk stockings with buckles on his shoes and breeches. At 5'2" you might have mistaken him in this dress for an itinerant preacher, rather than the acknowledged father of our constitution. He was a brilliant intellectual on every level.

"Indeed, it is grim," Madison said. "In the end, our success will depend on our civilian militia to resist the British at every turn, both on the open field and by employing every guerrilla tactic available. As you know, our military force is small compared to that of the British. and theirs is a force that has been well seasoned in the art of war against Napoleon.

"They have already been victorious in Europe, and it will take our every strength, and the grace of God, to defeat them here.

"With God and courage, yes, we will defeat them. We will do it as we did in our Revolutionary War for liberty and independence some forty years ago.

"But let me defer to our friend here, Colonel Monroe, who has done so well under my administration. I have recently decided to make him my Secretary of War, immediately. We all know him as a soldier of great courage. He has shown his mettle in previous wars and would know better than anyone else the dangers and how to meet them on our road to victory over the English."

Monroe had been standing off to the side when we turned towards him.

His was an imposing figure of strength and grace even though he was not dressed in military uniform. Still, he was universally recognized beyond Jefferson and Madison as one of the leaders and heroes of the War for Independence. But, for now, he had chosen a sort of French dress. It was a style he had acquired while serving in France with Jefferson. He wore dark breeches, silk hose, and pumps fashioned with buckles. I must say I would like to have seen him in his military dress. Nevertheless, he maintained that stern military bearing and the confident look in his eye as he addressed us projecting his very courage and determination.

But before Monroe could speak, Jupiter, who was Jefferson's favorite house servant, announced that dinner was ready, and he ushered us from the veranda into the dining room. Colonel Monroe's viewpoint on the State of the Union was delayed until after dinner.

### A Jeffersonian Dinner

Jefferson stood at the head of the table while Madison was at the foot. Monroe and I were across from each other in the middle.

"Gentlemen, please sit," said Jefferson. "Our kitchen has prepared our best for you. I hope it serves you well."

We were offered a veritable feast. There was a round of beef, cutlets of mutton, rice soup, macaroni pie, both French wine and champagne were cooling. Ice cream and Jefferson's coffee were to come later.

Yet another house servant – I did not know his name – served multiple courses from this feast. Glasses were filled with water, and goblets with wine or champagne to your taste.

We knew Jefferson did not drink anything but water during dinner. But, as it was his custom, he encouraged us to enjoy the wine and champagne throughout, which we were all happy to do.

Over the course of dinner, there was much reminiscence of the old days, mostly self-deprecating, each man modestly accepting compliments from the other.

Jefferson turned to Monroe on his right and said, "You, Sir, are a hero of the revolution. While it is true I had something to do with the foundation of our country, none of it would have mattered unless brave soldiers like you, as commanded by Washington, battled and defeated the enemy and, in your case, suffered grievous wounds for the survival of our country. I am so glad you are with us now, especially in light of the coming British invasion. You will see us through it."

"Indeed, that is true," said Madison, who by this time had been president for more than three years and was even then, August 14, 1814, facing that same imminent invasion. He turned to Monroe and spoke, "I value your experience on the field and your integrity and courage. May I say to you in confidence of the three other members present in our party, that I intend to make you my Secretary of War in the immediate future. As you know, we must go back to Washington to set up defenses against what may be a British attack on our very capital.

"I am also hopeful that our beleaguered military, combined with all of our citizen militants, will be able to hinder, and ultimately, stop and defeat the British advance and send them scurrying back to their ships to leave our shores."

"I assure you, Mr. President," said James Monroe to Madison, "it would be my honor and privilege to serve you in any way."

Then Madison turned to Jefferson. "And you, sir, are too modest. If George Washington is the father of our country, you, sir, remain its very spirit. In all that you have written, all those you have inspired, eight years of a signature presidency in which you doubled the size of our country…"

"Stop, Mr. President," said the former president to the current President Madison. "You flatter me too much. At this very time, you are holding together a country under both imminent attack and the risk of secession, both of which I believe you will meet successfully. You will afford us the same success you brought to us in your overseeing of the making of our Constitution."

These exchanges rang in my ears as I contemplated the conception, the beginning, and the current status of our country, all of which had taken place in the first 25 years of its life. And now its very future was to be determined by these three men. Everything was in their hands.

Jefferson took a few sips of the French wine that had been poured by Jupiter. This we all knew was the signal that dinner was coming to an end. Jupiter reappeared, as if by magic, and pulled back Jefferson's chair for him as he began to stand.

As he was about to disappear through the door to the kitchen, I asked Jupiter, as if in jest, if he enjoyed his position at Monticello.

He smiled and said, "Yes, sir, Mr. Coles, I love workin' in the house of Mr. Jefferson."

"Does he treat you well?" I asked with a wink.

"Oh yes, sir," said Jupiter, as he was retreating through the door to the kitchen, "After all, I'm family."

After a brief silence, Jefferson spoke, "Yes, Jupiter is family indeed, I don't know what I would do without him." Jefferson stood up and we three followed suit.

"Alright gentleman," he said, "let us repair to the parlor. I believe Jupiter will be bringing us some excellent coffee. Of course, you may also have port or brandy, if you prefer."

"And there," Jefferson said, smiling in my direction, "we will have a discussion with our young friend (me) about his plans to take his slaves to the Illinois territory to emancipate them."

### The Parlor

As we filed into the parlor, I noticed the fire was going. Even though it was August, we could feel the coolness of the evening.

Jefferson's one continual complaint was that he constantly felt the chill. This is why he purchased this particular fireplace, which is called the Rumford. It produced less smoke, more warmth, and additional light.

There were many portraits hung from the walls, statesmen and visionaries like John Locke, who was one of Jefferson's favorites. Also, there was other artwork that Jefferson had gathered from here and abroad. The floor was a hard parquet, and a beautiful view of the surrounding forest was evident through a central window.

Jupiter offered various after-dinner drinks to the rest of us, just as he brought a cup of Jefferson's favorite imported coffee to him.

Jefferson sat in his customary chair near the fire while President Madison and myself sat in armchairs facing him from across the room. In that moment, Colonel Monroe chose to stand, leaning on the mantle just beyond the flame of the fireplace.

Jefferson spoke first. "We are fortunate indeed to be in each other's company at a time when the country is at war with the British and when one of our fellow states, Massachusetts, is threatening to secede from our country in order to make a separate peace with the British. But I believe that, even as a young country our democracy has the courage, the resolve, and the intelligence to meet and defeat our adversaries. We are doing, and

we will do, whatever is necessary to keep Massachusetts and the rest of New England in the fold and drive the British from our shores once more.

"But there is another terrible problem which has plagued our society from the beginning. Slavery. It has troubled me from the start. Mr. Coles here believes he may have resolved the problem, at least as it has to do with the emancipation of his *own* slaves."

Jefferson continued, "He can enlighten us here of his position and perhaps, we, him."

Mr. Jefferson turned to me and spoke, "Mr. Coles, I would ask you to speak first, as you did with me in your correspondence, on how you hope to end all slavery in our country and, that in the meantime, you will do it individually and immediately by way of emancipating your own slaves.

"After you speak, I would ask our President Madison and then Colonel Monroe to respond with their own thoughts on the subject.

"Mr. Coles, you have said yours is a mission inspired by God himself. And I believe you believe that. But let me say here that I am hoping that this will be a fruitful conversation which will lead to a practical pathway towards a gradual emancipation of all slaves and then perhaps even a repatriation of the freed slaves to their former country.

"I implore all of us here present that this be a private conversation between ourselves and not for the members of the public at large. That would bring nothing but harm to the cause and its revolution. At this stage, our conversation could be willfully misunderstood by those who are in opposition to our goal. Now, I assume we are all in agreement, Messrs. Coles, Madison, Monroe and myself?"

We all nodded as Jefferson himself stretched out his long legs on his chair in his usual informal way. He extended a hand in my direction and said, "Alright Mr. Coles, please give us your thoughts, your convictions and resolution, in ridding us all of the anathema of slavery. Please proceed."

And that's how it began.

I stood up to face my distinguished audience. I remember the penetrating heat of the fire at my backside. Colonel Monroe had taken a seat in the chair closest to Madison, leaving Jefferson an easy view of the three of us.

---

Now, my family, you already know my position on this issue. I proceeded to present it again to my three companions at Monticello on that night in August of 1814. I have held it all of my adult life since the transformative power of God came upon me in my second year at William and Mary College.

I told my three "wise men," as I have told you over the years, that I became convinced that it was the will of God that I renounce slavery as immoral – that Black people should never be considered property and that holding slaves was a dangerous breach of virtue, dangerous to the republic and dangerous to the very concept of individual freedom on which our republic was founded.

I told them that it might indeed be difficult to end slavery, but since man himself had created slavery, certainly he could find a way to end it.

Further, I told them that I believe that slavery would ultimately corrupt the Republic itself because it deprived a portion of its own people of their very liberty.

Finally, I told them I *did* prefer that collective action be taken by the State, but since the State had neglected to do its duty all of these years, I would set out alone. At this point I had already made plans to take my sixty slaves from Virginia to the free territory of Illinois. There, I said, I would emancipate them all and help them get established in their new state of freedom. Finally, I told them I would begin that freedom journey in January of the following year (1815) or as soon as possible and hopefully prove the example to other slave holders that they could follow me.

I concluded by apologizing to Jefferson, Madison, and Monroe, all my friends and mentors, for the abruptness of my candor and thanked them for their indulgence.

There was a silence as I returned to my chair.

Slowly, President Madison pulled himself up in his chair whose very commodiousness tended to cover up his small frame. But now, he was sitting bolt upright. The fire in his eyes belied the soft voice which emanated.

"Edward, you and I have often spoken of the inequity of this slavery business. In all this time you have served as my private secretary, I have respected you and your vision absolutely. Apart from all else, you know that I hold you in deep esteem. You are close to my heart. Now I ask you to indulge my own response to your presentation."

---

Sadly, I had heard it all before. Madison concluded his narration by pleading with me to stay on as his personal secretary until the end of his term before proceeding with my own plans.

In this time of war I could not deny him of his request that I stay on in his administration even as I knew it would delay my commitment to free my slaves.

Colonel Monroe repeated his earlier advice that I should delay any emancipation of my slaves until such time as there was more public support and that, in any event, I would need that support for my larger mission of ending emancipation in general.

Jefferson was as I had heard him before in our correspondence, eloquent but with no solution save that it be something my generation would have to solve.

*Goodbye*

Dear family, I remember once again how I felt when I said my goodbyes to Jefferson, Madison and Monroe. They were pleasant and heartfelt, but still a certain sadness permeated the atmosphere. We all felt it. Nothing had been resolved, save for my concession to Madison that I would delay my emancipation trip until the end of his term. I knew he needed me and I could not refuse him.

Sadly, even as I was able to free my slaves in 1819, nothing but the Civil War fifty years later finally ended slavery by way of Lincoln's Emancipation Proclamation.

There is still the history and chronology of how I completed my God given mission to free my slaves and what I did to end slavery elsewhere, wherever I could.

My time in this world is coming to a close, I fear. Perhaps it is my vanity, but I want you to understand my life and what I did with it.

*Chronology*

You know that I served as President Madison's private secretary from 1809 until 1815.

In 1816, he asked me to be his personal envoy to Russia. I could not refuse, though as I said before, this would delay my intended trip to Illinois to emancipate my slaves.

In 1819, finally, I was able to take my some sixty slaves to the free territory of Illinois, to emancipate them, and to deed each adult male over the age of twenty-three, 160 acres from farmland I had purchased. This was to make sure that they would have an economic base to grow their newfound freedom.

In 1822, I was elected Governor of Illinois and, together with my anti-slavery colleagues, we were able to defeat all efforts to change the Illinois constitution in order to permit slavery again.

After my Governorship, the forces of pro-slavery strengthened and in 1830, I was defeated in my bid for Congress.

In 1832, because of this continuing hostile climate, I moved to Philadelphia where I had many friends who felt as committed as I did towards ending slavery everywhere.

Here, in Philadelphia, I had the good fortune to court and marry your mother (your grandmother) who was born Sally Logan Roberts.

For over thirty years she and I have enjoyed a wonderful life together of which you my children and grandchildren have been a major part. We have been truly blessed.

My biggest sadness, which has all but broken my heart, was the death of my son Roberts in 1862 at the battle of Roanoke Island. He joined the Confederacy because he believed his first duty was to defend his State and his homeland. I respect the courage of his convictions and I miss him terribly.

It is my hope that President Lincoln's emancipation of slavery in 1863 will be acknowledged and enforced throughout the country.

In parting I ask you to never forget the anti-slavery crusade that dominated my life. I ask that you make it part of yours.

*Edward Coles*
January, 1868
Philadelphia

# A FREEDOM MEETING
## 90 Years after the Death of Edward Coles
### *Keswick Virginia*

In 1958, a well-dressed Black woman knocked on our front door. Since our farming community just north of Charlottesville had seen much easy commerce between the races, this was not unusual. Perhaps she was there to seek a job or to ask if we could help her find a relation. It didn't matter. She was welcomed into our house. I was about six at the time and I witnessed it all.

The woman asked me if my mother was Mrs. Coles, and when I said yes, she asked if she could speak with her for a few minutes. My mother, who was always welcoming, brushed by me to open the door for our visitor. Mother ushered her into the parlor where she asked her if she would like some tea. Our visitor (whose name I have forgotten) smiled and accepted.

I remember they sat there with their tea, just smiling at one another. Then my mother asked her, quietly, what it was she had come to speak to us about.

It turns out she was the great-great-great granddaughter of one of the sixty slaves my great-great-great uncle, Edward Coles, had freed way back in 1819 – not only freed but provided every male over the age of 23 a tract of his own land.

This Black lady wanted my family, the descendants of Edward Coles, to know that his gift of emancipation had produced lawyers and doctors and soldiers and businessmen in her family for generations, all because of the freedom and land that our ancestor had provided them so many years ago.

It turns out that our visitor, a high school teacher herself, had traveled from her home in Illinois all the way down to our farm when she discovered that we were direct descendants of Edward Coles and would be able to find us.

"I simply wanted to come down and thank you. And I wanted you to know how much good Mr. Edward Coles had done for us." She then got up as if to leave us and when my mother asked her if she would like a ride, she said that she had left her taxi waiting outside because she did not want to take up too much of our time but needed to get back to the bus station for her trip back to Illinois. My mother immediately said that she would be glad to take our visitor to the station.

"Oh, no, ma'am, I don't want to be a burden. I just wanted to share the gift of success that we owe to your ancestor, Mr. Edward Coles. So thank you from the bottom of my heart."

With that she disappeared through the screen door.

---

**Author's Note:**
**A Fireside Chat** is historical fiction. The character descriptions and events of the time and the conversations are authentic, based on primary materials. Only the common setting is imagined.

*Love is what we're here for . . .*

# POETRY

# Growing Up

## CLOTHES FOR THE BOY
## ARMOR FOR THE MAN

I used to worry a lot about growing up.
Every time I was told to cherish my childhood because too soon I'd grow up,
I said I didn't want to grow up at all.

I wanted to keep wearing my khaki shorts and black
Super Ked sneakers and my Washington Senators cap.
I wanted to keep pounding on my Gil McDougald Fielders mitt.

So, I remained immature, irresponsible and emotionally lazy
for as long as I could.
But the other day I realized, to my shock and surprise I had grown up.
Despite my best efforts to avoid decisions of finality and conviction.
I have learned:
– how to send the kids to camp
– how to pay the monthly rent,
– and how to avoid everlasting debt.

Now, I plan for the future
on how to make others believe in me,
even when I don't believe in myself.

Now,
I put on my tropical tan summer suit, my oxblood Gucci loafers,
my button-down blue Brooks Brothers shirt,
my Paul Stewart multi-striped tie and
my casual cool demeanor.
It's a little harder to dress for adulthood.

But still, and in my mind,
I'm still pounding on my patented
Gil McDougald Fielders mitt.

## FOCUS CYCLE

I was
fresh out of school,
back with the boys
who know too much
to know so little.

They have theory and hope,
and calculated cool,
they are nobody's fools.

They are
pure and straight.
They are college freight;
what they can conceive,
their innocence will believe.

Experience has taught me
to stand back and wait
-to hesitate-
to seal my fate.

…. and I say,

"Fiery vision, fanned by
youth,
will you not learn from me?

Clear water ideologue
turns murky brown
when mixed with the blood
of life."

## YOUTHFUL VISION

As the rays of a rising sun light the new day,
Coleman lifts his arms to stretch.
He makes his bed with gusto,
leaves his bear and pajamas under the sheets.
Coleman is eight.

Coleman works on words.
He hears of battles in Grenada,
wonders of helicopters and rocket launchers.
He explains Grenada to his friend as he imagines it;
"it's where they make bombs and
Grenada grenades."

Coleman asked me if he died today.
"Yes," I said. "Our Great Pyrenees is gone.
It was time. His body was old and his spirit was ready to fly."
"Don't tell me again," he said. "I've had my cry."
Coleman is eight. He's learned to say good-bye.

We sat alone in a hard, wooden pew of the brand-new church.
I watched a friend give his first sermon – on Sainthood,
while Coleman saw his young son, Jake, the acolyte, who sat just
past the altar and was dressed in white.
And when we emerged to the cool autumn air,
Coleman allowed that it was all quite good
and nicely short,

…but then he said
"The lady up front sang a little bit loud and a little bit off."
Coleman is eight. He's learned perspective.

## SHE'S 15

She's 15 and so misunderstood:
she's willful, defiant and bold,
but she's pretty cute too.
She's a bobtailed, brown-eyed beauty.
She's 5 foot 4, and reaching for more.
She has flashing eyes and horse-riding thighs.

She sees the world in absolute hues
of black and white, no greys will she choose.
She's really hot or really cold,
and we adults are much too old
to understand
her clarity of view.

But she knows as she sees you
that she's not too young to be undone
by what made you wiser.
Her truth can be erased
by facts so arranged they
yield a convenient refrain.

And she knows,
somewhere in her soul,
that time and experience
are really the foe
of her clarity of view.

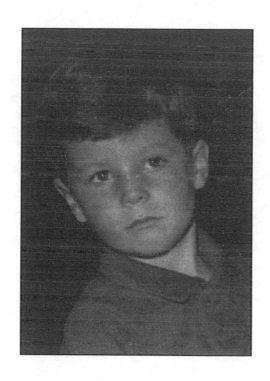

# Love and Friendship

## CHOICES

Vines with intertwining strength
that grow towards the sky
can grow apart,
seeking separate paths
… and smother what went before.

Are we old friends, grown apart,
or do we still nourish and replenish
the other?

Do we reach for the Heavens
together,
or do we kill the remembered spirit?
Do we start to pull apart?

Friends must maintain a mighty
vigil.
Are we support vines, do we still
intertwine,
or not?
Have we crossed the line?

Hold the goodness of the past,
and make it last.
Keep old friends old friends.
Let the spirit never part.

# A FRIEND

As a gentle breeze whispers to a sail,
so a friend listens, advises, but does not judge.

The sun rises every day to light the dark,
and a friend returns to cheer the heart.

An old woolen nightgown warms but does not chafe,
so a friend surrounds you with good thoughts, but does not shout.

As a tickling furry feather can make you erupt in involuntary laughter,
a friend consoles your heavy heart and helps you smile.

The heart speaks to the body
as a friend warms your thoughts and helps you understand.

The clear sky, high above the storm clouds,
is ready to wrap the world in velvet blue,
a friend is too. Whether challenged, tested or obscured,
his living faith abides in you.

## STARTING OVER AGAIN

Now that she's gone…
I'm starting all over again.

I'm going to rearrange the furniture;

I'll put my desk near the window and light –

And I'll use this straight back chair
to sit and write
… as I begin again.

\* \* \* \* \*

I'll see the dawn's reflected light
just outside my window.
The morning sun will spread throughout the hills.

It gives me hope for a better day,
And, even though my heart breaks,
I will take this pen and begin again.

## WHEN ROB* CAME CALLING
*a free verse daydream*

The other night, Rob Coles dropped by
just to say hi.
"What's new in your world?
How's your week shaping up?" he said.
When I asked him, "how ya feeling?"
He said, "Good, good, I'm feeling great,"
even though the last time I saw him I knew he was dying.

"You know, Rob, you should have run for Mayor," I said.
"With your kind and funny people loving ways,
you would have won."
But he said, "No.
Life's too much fun for doing that."
And he roared with laughter,
and his eyes twinkled
at the mere thought of being Mayor.

"I'm thinking about you down there," he said.
"But I love playing Jefferson,
while hanging around up here. It's all pretty cool,
and I get laughter
in all the right places."

"Yes," Rob said, "It's all pretty good,
and the food is outstanding.
You really should come up.
But finish what you're doing down there,
first."

"And when you come up
I'll introduce you to the good stuff,

the love and laughter and goodliness.
Yes, we'll have a lot of fun and
the tennis is always good up here.
And, in this thin, clean air, your golf ball goes forever."

Rob tipped the wide-brimmed Panama hat
he borrowed from me a few years before,
and, with a mischievous grin
disappeared into that Heavenly thin air.

I know I'll see him soon - but not too soon -
I've got work to do down here.
Maybe you do too.
But when I get up there to see my friend,
I'm gonna get my wide-brimmed Panama hat back,
and maybe we'll play a little tennis,
and have a pint or two.

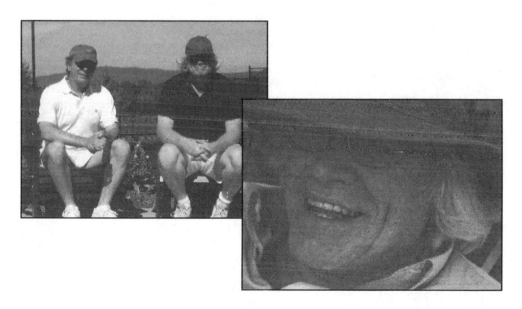

*Rob Coles was my good friend, and a fifth-generation direct-descendent of Thomas Jefferson.
He portrayed Jefferson in local, regional, and national venues for many years. He died much too early at
the age of 61 on September 17, 2013. This poem was inspired by a dream.*

## THE MISTRESS'
## GENTLEMAN SHEEPDOG

When he was young he would race across the hayfield
and come to a screeching halt
at the open door of her car
and give a hoarse yodel of joy
as his mistress did emerge.

In his middle-age he learned to cradle his bowl,
paws surrounding,
as he looked for ambush
from his younger friends.

As he grew older, he took precautions.
Legs are stiffer
in the bloom of seniority.

And now, at twelve,
he quietly awaits his vetly turn.
He submits with calm to prodding and pricking.
He trusts his mistress who holds him close.

He is a gentleman and will not bite
the white coated man.

There are people tonight; he moves slowly
down the hall to the bedroom.
He lowers his rigid frame onto
the oriental rug at the side
of his mistress' bed.

She arrives.
Slowly, he rolls onto his back
and paws the air playfully
with the hope of one more pat
or a soothing scratch behind the ear.

Slowly, and despite the pain,
he lifts his head in joy.
Suddenly, he falls back,
and he is gone.

But,
in her moments of sadness,
in her feeling so dark,
his mistress remembers the brightness
and the joy he did bring her;
love and fun and dignified laughter
was Justin, her gentleman sheepdog.

## FANDANGO BLUE

In
Fandango Blue
I saw all this
from a magic tavern by the sea.

I had my back to the fire.

The warmth did transport me
through the winds in the harbor
and the watery fish below
up past the boats to the
dancing clouds above.

I moved past the wavy blues
and saw through the horizon
and looked through a window
way above the dolphins and the boats
below
to the clear green and
crystal blue
light
of happy thoughts
of Fandango Blue and you.


*For Marjorie*

*Thank you, Jane Goodall*

# Overcoming Life

# SALAAM!

Waiting in the zoo
is a thing I like to do.
But I can always leave
the animals in the zoo.

I would hate to be
a mammal,
who is caged
and waiting
for a break
in his day.

Perhaps a tourist will
drop by
to describe for him
a far away place;
but I think not.

Does he yearn
for freedom
of choice or simply
for freedom?

…Salaam!
You are not in the zoo.
You have a choice and a chance.
Will you take it,
or let it get away?

Come to your own chosen salvation.
Give up the waiting
and anticipating.

Find the courage
to reach out
and take the offer
to live anew.
Salaam!

# THE LIGHTNESS OF WATER

The lumbering walrus man
wears his shawl
of 300 pounds.

He lurches around the pool,
finds the steps
and lowers himself down,
slowly, painfully, arthritically,
with every rung.

But then, ever so slowly,
as he pushes out into water
and loses 100 pounds of weight,
a smile comes over his face.
He has now reached his very own
state of grace.

# DANCING IN THE MOONLIGHT

George Herman Ruth and Muhammad Ali,
powerful skills had they.
With the flick of a wrist or the flash of an eye,
the ball left the park, the glove made its mark,
for George Herman Ruth and Muhammed Ali.

Ruth was a big-handed moon man
talking with style and a smooth chocolate smile
that was Ali.
But when the timing was right in a moment of light,
they transcended their skills with the might of their wills.

Their Peter Pan faith and colliding timing
will conquer
those insurmountable, unaccountable…
Captain Hook odds…
that crushed the skills of lesser wills.

George Herman Ruth and Muhammed Ali
were magical mythmaking men.
a pre-pointed smash to the bleachers
or a knockout punch to overreachers,
we glowed in the bright of their radiant light.

George Herman Ruth and Muhammed Ali
took us along…
as we danced in their moonlight.

## MIDDIE

Liquid blue eyes resolve.
Gnarled hands push.
Wheels roll,
slowly;

across the tracks,
below the bridge,
past the parked cars
and the watching eyes;

to the pick up
of her papers
on the mall brick
by the bank.

Eighty pounds and 66,
back propped up on pillowed chair,
her two wheels work for two legs lost.

Liquid blue eyes resolve.
Strongly, firmly, arm extending,
and with worthful purpose she declaims:
 "PAPER HERE!"

It's not what happens to you that matters.
It's what you do with what happens to you that matters.

## THE WATER OF LIFE

No matter how hard you try
to tiptoe through the morning dew,
a little bit of wet
will always find
its way
to
you.

## THE DREAM BEHIND THE WALL OF FEAR

Frustration-fear/anger turned inward,
Opaque eyes that see nothing,
crippled thoughts kept in lard
lose their rhythm and rhyme.

But

As you face your fears,
suddenly the wall explodes;
the dragon stands alone.
Fever slows. The fear is no longer unknown.

Hands reach out, and fear dragons
disappear in the clear truth
that while you're still on your own
you are not alone.

# Still Crazy

(After All These Years – *Paul Simon*)

## THE WASHING UP ROOM
## THE EYES, THE EYES

I stand in front of the wash basin, surrounded
by gray walls and harsh light and the closed face of a nurse.
She is impatient to make us
go to bed and to end her shift.

"Go on, Charlie," she says, "and brush your teeth."
She is also my counselor who I thought had understood.
"Take your Lithium.
 Rest. Relax. You'll be all right."

Do these empty words mean more confinement?
"OK," I said, "but I've left my toothpaste on my bed".
"Oh, all right." She says with an empty smile and leaves my side to fetch it.

I turn and look at the eyes of the others,
milling around the washing up room.
We are herded like sightless sheep, numbed
in our pen and wearing our pale green pajama smocks.

It is their eyes that scare me:
anxious eyes that do not see me,
hostile eyes that see only inner anger,
or vacant eyes reflecting my face and seeing nothing.

Not guards, not patients, not counselors, but eyes.
I must escape to save my eyes.

## DO GOOD AND PREVAIL

Never look for forgiveness.
You'll not always find it
on your search
for the Holy Grail.

"Step aside young tot,"
The Imperial Guard was fed up.
Countless implosions, excessive defecations
and needless decapitations; all were
the customary treatments
of the patients at
Blue Ridge Psychiatric Hospital.
Nurse Whipple, who curled her
hair each morning before
work, was a proponent of
all the aforementioned treatments.

"They say you are insane,"
said Whipple.
"So, what is left," I say.
"Nothing," she said, "But to
be good and obey the rules."
"Screw you" I said.
And she left the room.
I said, if only to myself,
Do Good and Prevail
it's the only Way.
Do good and pray.
Love, work, and pray . . .
To God
and to Good.
It's the only way . . .
to the Holy Grail.

# HELLO MARGUERITE

Hello Marguerite,
I'm stuck in old Blue Ridge,
Hospital that is,
again.

So, here we are, the Samurai Warriors,
searching for the reason for being,
when it suddenly became clear,
that it was all up to me
to discover the meaning of life.

As it is with everyone,
I need courage to overcome fear of being here
and to follow my heart.

Still
an insane asylum seems to be
as good a place as any to start.

And so, Marguerite,
I have just had my hearing
from the people
of small soul who fear what used to be their hearts.

You can imagine the results…
there is no release without playing the part
of remorse for my small faults
and acceptance of their small truths.
Well, as you know, Marguerite, I am a very good actor
and I really did want to get out…
So, will I see you tonight?

Your very own Samurai Warrior

Faith

## CHERISH THE YOU

Actors project
what others might do;
but you should elect
to be only you.

Some guys try
so hard to be cool,
only to learn
it's a full time job
to be nobody's fool.

One day you'll see
the best you can be
is to be the best you.
I said YOU. BOO!

Evolving, some solving,
but always revolving
'round you, Lou.

It's the only skin
you're in…you are
the Original.

Only you
can be
the best you
you can be.

Only you.
No one else can ever be
the best you
you can be.

Cherish the you.

# ETERNITY

You cannot wager on
eternity.
That is a bet
HE will not let;
those cards will bring
certain death… to ye
of little Faith.

Is it so that
I must leave you?
You are the best
that I have known…
but the seed is sown.

You do not see
that we're on loan,
and that everything you own
will not save you,
will not save you.

Your fears,
your very own fears,
and your silence,
will bring on the years
of pain and silence.

…
They belong to those
who would disown you…

So, who are you?
      Now!

# THE GIVING THING

Love comes from above,
then within.
It's an unrelenting thing
…a giving thing.

It comes from your soul,
the harmony of faith and you;
it's in your life.

It's real LOVE
unconditional,
love;
Agapé
Love;
No sequé
Love.

Whether it's close or from afar,
it knows no bar.
…and it always knows, as you do,
why you do
what you do;
and what you grew.
It's good love.
It's God's love!!

# THE MEANING OF LIFE

*forty days and back*

By June first it was the worst:
love congealed in all my hopes,
and yes, there were the tropes, the usual dopes,
lawyers, bankers, and other reality types.

They did their best
to bring me down-
"Straighten up. Fly right-
take your medicine or
get out of town."

I did.

But I fooled 'em
'cuz I came back
to give them all the sack,
and now I'm going to kick ass and take numbers.

There'll be lots of fallen timber,
wooden soldiers who
play at life,
self-righteous hypocrites and other
self serving shits.

And then there are the do gooders
who give to get,
yet none of them have truly
given yet.

They don't get it,
but you will.
Pour yourself a smile
and give the world some joy.

'cuz I'm tellin' you boys and girls,
before you leave this world,
you better learn the
meaning of life.

And it ain't that three-piece suit
you wear to earn that two bit loot-
money.

Money ain't nothing honey,
nothing at all.
And you'll be appalled
that you really can't
take it with you, son…
…and that's no fun…

Forget the pearls, girls;
they'll stay in this world.

So what is left
of this thing you call life
that you can take into the next one?

Listen up,
people.
Pay attention to
the steeple…
and what it means.

…Not the minister
sometimes sinister
in his contriving goodness…

And oh, you Pharisees,
your glib, self-righteousness
will get you nowhere
squared.

Come to the steeple
and the love of all people.
Listen up!
The secret of life,
from this world to the next,
is LOVE,
a pure, simple, hard giving,
a little more selfless sort of
LOVE.

A little bit better
a little bit brighter than before.
LOVE!

# THE OPEN HAND CALENDAR

The hand of life opens at
    birth.
It then begins to close.
January is renewed hope.
February doesn't last so long.
March is a harbinger of
    spring.
April begins life itself.
May's warmth prepares the
    coming heat.
June is graduation and hot
    starts.
July brings steamy sidewalks
    and cool pools.
August is taking time out.
September calls us back.
October is leaves falling
and summer plans laid bare.
November disappears in a
    flurry of anticipation.
December is the end of the
    beginning again.
And the advent of faith
    that
        every hand that closes
        will one day open
        again.

## EASTER

It's your seventh Easter son,
one on which to rejoice and have fun,
to be glad we are all as one.

But think, too, what else it means,
that egg does more than hold jelly beans –
it is rebirth, a renaissance of the nativity scene.

To think of others when setting goals,
strive to reach, like the first standing foal
and always love, and believe,
have faith in your soul.

From Easter to Christmas and round again
it will always see you through.

## SAVING THE REST OF US

Who will save the souls of the children
      if not the will of us all?

What does it mean, the murders
      of Christ, of Joan and of Paul?

The lover who loves, the hater who hates,
      the sinner, the sin, the beast in the best
            of us.

Who made this malcontents world
      will if one save will all save.

What was good, gone bad through hurt, luck and greed
      or battered innocents, who bleed just to breathe.

As we all go to ground and finally to fossil,
      He will have us all
      as his dearest apostle.

Anointed bread or roughest leaven
      God will have us in His heaven.

To His heaven, to his heaven,
      Even those of roughest leaven.

Nantucket

## NANTUCKET IN SEASON

Winter drives away the Summer masses.
Fall leads to the Christmas Stroll,
after which they'll all be gone
but just the native few.

You'll breathe again, Nantucket,
with cold and frost and ice;
fresh air and Arctic winds will
drive life inside or underground.

 You'll sleep again, Nantucket
'till Spring calls forth your beauty.
You'll be incredibly clean for the blues,
for the boats and the beach seeking masses.

Give them their pleasures, yield to their smiles
'till the sweet, cold breath of winter cleanses
our far away isle.

## NANTUCKET EVENING

As the sweet, salty spray retraces my face
and the fog rolls in from the Moor,
I hear wind whirling wisps of Nantucket lace;
sight lost to sound, to touch and to fate.

## NANTUCKET MORN

As sand from the weathered pebble and rock
glimmers to grey blue on the ever-brightening horizon,
I see seagulls who soar and glide
in cloudless free breezes.

I feel
cool water ooze of bay
beneath my feet;
the salty spray awakens my lips,
caresses my nose.
Both are hungry for
the smells
of the sea.

I see now the sun has appeared
rising up like a Kellogg's pop tart
bursting over the Horizon
with such flashing color
of iridescent white to crimson red,
then fades to blue and grey
again.

The flat ripples of the ocean
begin to shimmer too,
as each day begins.

And
I thank God for the chance
 to be reborn
 in the light
of the love I see
on this Nantucket morn.

## LEAVING NANTUCKET IN A BUBBLE OF GREEN

They eat the lobster bisque.
They buy the Lilly Pulitzer
and they lobby at the Knobby
shop in Nantucket.

Soon they will fly
on down to Bahamas
to consult with their Lamas.

Or sail down south
to somewhere else
warm and fashionable.

…perhaps Key West
when Nantucket grows cold
and the numbness surrounds them.

The money is there
to take them away
in a mist of control,
a bubble so bold
it can carry their load
of insulation.
It's like their Visa card
which is never rejected,
it's the color of green;
money, that is.

It brings velvet smooth clues
to the fashionable hues
all leading nowhere
…comfortably.

This
bubble of green,
which rolls and cajoles them,
as it also controls them.
It's that good feeling,
brainnumbing,
know nothing
bubble of green.

Come Fall, it's time to roll them on
out of here.
Please.

# Lesser Gods

## LAWYERS REJOICE

Hooray!
There's been a drug bust.
A plane has crashed in St. Clair,
and the pilot's a lush.
A lawsuit's a must.

Lawyers rejoice!
Divorces arise
from lust and from lies.
The practice can work either side.

Justice and integrity
have long since died
in the master plan,
where every lawyer wins
when money's the name
of the advocacy game.

So, lawyers rejoice!
O.J. went free.
But you've earned your fee,
for money's the name
of the advocacy game.

## THE PEOPLES' SNOBBERY

People feel better when they are comfortable
in their little universe of
competence and mini omnipotence.

They stand back with their fellow confidants,
to trade those near quiet snipes
about the less fortunate who surround them.

It's a form of grace
affordable to all with a few friends
and a pair of blinders.

## BURPALICIOUS

I know that burgers and hot dogs,
and fries on the side
are not good for me.

But they sure are burpalicious.

All beef patties, special sauce,
Buried under lots of limp lettuce
on a sesame seed bun.
Oh yeah.

They are so burpalicious.

Now I know you know
I don't know
where this is
going.

Perhaps it's to fried chicken or encrusted fish.
All make my cholesterol rise,
But who cares,

I'll order another side of fries.

Because it's all burpalicious.

Now, please pass me the Rolaids.

Life's like that.
It can be burpalicious too.
But, in life we're required to learn a lot
and live a lot

and digest things that are not so
burpalicious.

Life's often more vicious
and non-nutritious.
Often it is not burpalicious.

But when everyone is fat and happy,
never feeling crappy
from too much nutrition
you can always go
one step further…
to Cracker Barrel

Where life is but a dream
it's all burpalicious,
and you don't have to do the dishes.

Imagine you're at Burger King
where everything is sublime
including your waistline.
It will grow in proportion to every bite you take
to every breath you make.

It's all burpalicious.

# Getting Old

# OLD ROCKERS

Ravaged faces
embrace the traces
of the distant past.

The gravelly voices
still sing the lines
of melody and rhymes
which bring back memories
of earlier times.

See the creases,
the wrinkles and the sunken pieces,
are all belied by the rhythm,
the melody and the rhyme.

It's the story of life,
and the passions of our past.
All are pounding to the beat,
the remembered truths
of a distant youth.

The music stays true.
Rock 'n Roll never dies.
It's a little bit of you
and a little bit of me
…too.

## REMEMBRANCE

Rippling in at low tide or
crashing through the sands of time,
I hurdled through that systolic door,
Triggered by a flash of insight or seeping through a crack …

Despite the way things were, or the way I thought they were,
and the things I hoped to be but aren't,
there remains the ever-ticking time machine.

Still, there's life and what I really did,
a moment of bravery in a life of cowardice,
a little bit of truth reshaped by me,
so that others could see it clear.

Through dreams and hopes and everlasting schemes,
I still look forward to looking back and
hope I'll have the time and thought
worth having in those waves of remembrance.

Were people better for touching me?
Did I make them blink?
Did I make them think
in the time I had
on the ever-ticking time machine?

## SLIPPING BACK

I am
slipping back into the womb of time
from whence I came.
I've become a blink
in someone else's eye,
perhaps a wink.

We are now
who we were
and where we came from
all those years ago.

The ether of time,
wafts sublime,
infinite,
infinitesimal.

Energy
is never lost.
It must go somewhere
as do I.

It takes me back to
where I'm born again,
received by the grace
of God,
or at least of Good.

Will I see you there?
Will I see you in the good love,
of God's love
and your love too?

## JOHN TUCK*
*An Elegy*

He is a tall and lanky man.
He wears a Scots beret and a silk ascot.
He leans against the bar,
inserts a thin cigar
into a silver holder and lights it up.

As the light blue eyes
fix to the top-hatted walrus
mounted on the opposite wall,
he begins to talk in a mellifluous accent
of New York/London baritone smoothness.

The nightly magic of "John Tuck Speak"
surrounds and uplifts us.
He transports us.
We are in his element,
at the Gaslight restaurant
in his palace of dreams.

The guests come to celebrate.
The famous and the rest of us,
Dylan and Baez, Garfunkel and Simon,
all are there for the magic.

The meandering dreams,
the beneficent schemes,
all reach to the rafters
in raucous laughter.

But wait...

Suddenly, he was gone,
drawn by the sickly sycophantic ether of a suicide ride.

Had he grown tired of
the ravages of time
or, perhaps, the fear of the fear
of living?

So, the card game was up.
The winners told jokes,
the losers went home,
and he said goodbye.

We'll miss his fire
and the wit of his light
but his words said so bright
are just echoes tonight.

What did he leave us,
reprieve or bereave us?
He left us some karma
and love of life's drama.

He left us all in the sadness of laughter,
all on his road to forever hereafter.
And we'll miss you tonight,
Mr. Tuck.

*John Tuck was founder and master of ceremonies at the Gaslight restaurant, circa 1961. He was my mother's first cousin. He died in a one car crash in 1983 when he chose to drive his car off a cliff of the Blue Ridge Mountains.

I believe he had grown tired of us all, though we wish he had stayed a little bit longer.

## RAISE THE GOOD THOUGHT

With fits and starts
you sputter and stop.
Gluey slow,
you pull unstuck
from resignation and constipated thought.
Then….
You break through tunnel vision
and "go along" syndrome.

Ear hear.
Eye see.
Tongue taste.
Nose smell.
Hand hold
….. Each time as if the first time …..
Prestidigitation
and craftsman's sweat
will create.

# FALL MIRAGE

I saw a dance of dogwood
waltzing in the breeze
of an orange/red dawn.

Quickly the fog
rose over the trees
and color palleted leaves.

It covered up the entire
Blue Ridge Mountain range.

Some weeks later
I looked again.
The early morning sun
had burned away the crystalized drops.

Bare black stick trees
stood defrocked, colorless,
bending in pain, one to the other,
whispering of better days to come,
but first the worst to pay.

*About the Author*

Alden Bigelow is a native of Charlottesville, Virginia, a writer and retired advertising executive. He moved to New York City in the 70s, where he worked for the Ogilvy and Mather Advertising Agency. He later returned to Charlottesville to start his own Agency which he ran for over 30 years.

Before writing *Waiting on Nantucket*, Bigelow wrote *Killing Time in a Small Southern Town* as historical fiction about the tumultuous times of early integration in Charlottesville. He also wrote *Norton's Lament*, a novel about a young man with psychological issues coming of age in an unknown and unsympathetic world. A fourth book, *Growing Up with Jemima*, is his whimsical true story of growing up with his dog in the 1950's in Charlottesville and Richmond, Virginia. Recently, Bigelow has also written a fifth book, *The Great American Mammal Jamboree*, a fable which deals with animal rights and the fight against animal abuse.

Bigelow holds a B.A. from California State University, Hayward, and a Master's Degree in Legal History from the University of Virginia. He is currently chairman of the Board of the Blue Ridge Writers.

He lives in Lake Monticello, Virginia with his wife, Marjorie, and their exceptional dog, Elvis. His son and daughter-in-law, Coleman and Maura, live in Maplewood, New Jersey, with 3 outstanding grandchildren, Molly, Ian and Maeve, and 2 fabulous dogs, Homer and Goose.